Vocabulary
in Context

FOR THE COMMON CORE STANDARDS

Grade
3

Table of Contents

Vocabulary in Context G3, SV 9780547625768

Vocabulary in Context G3, SV 9780547625768

Introduction

Steck-Vaughn's *Vocabulary in Context* series offers parents and educators high-quality, curriculum-based products that align with the Common Core Standards for English Language Arts for grades 2–9.

Each unit in the *Vocabulary in Context* books includes:

- fiction and/or nonfiction selections, covering a wide variety of topics

- context activities, ascertaining that children understand what they have read

- vocabulary activities, challenging children to show their understanding of key vocabulary

- questions in a standardized-test format, helping prepare children for standardized exams

- word skills activities, targeting additional vocabulary words and vocabulary skills

- writing activities, providing assignments that encourage children to use the vocabulary words

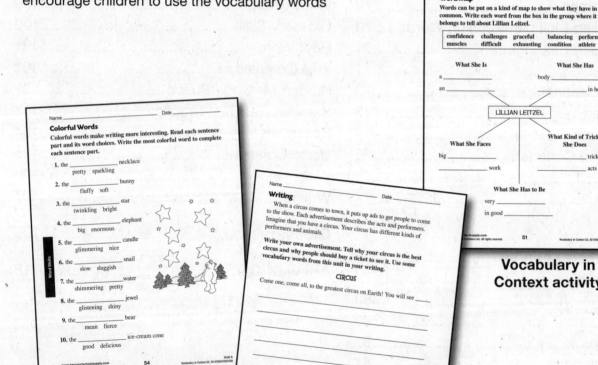

Reading selection

Vocabulary in Context activity

Word Skills activity

Writing activity

Introduction
Vocabulary in Context G3, SV 9780547625768

Homophones

Homophones are words that sound the same but have different meanings and usually have different spellings.

ant—aunt	groan—grown	right—write
ate—eight	heal—heel	road—rode—rowed
base—bass	here—hear	sail—sale
be—bee	hi—high	sea—see
beach—beech	hoarse—horse	seen—scene
bear—bare	hole—whole	sew—so—sow
beat—beet	hour—our	sight—cite—site
berry—bury	I—eye	some—sum
blew—blue	made—maid	son—sun
bored—board	meat—meet	sore—soar
bow—bough	new—knew	stair—stare
brake—break	no—know	steal—steel
buy—by	oar—or	their—there—they're
cell—sell	one—won	through—threw
cent—sent—scent	pail—pale	to—too—two
close—clothes	pain—pane	wail—whale
dear—deer	pair—pear	weak—week
flew—flu	peace—piece	we'll—wheel
flour—flower	peek—peak	wait—weight
for—four	plane—plain	way—weigh
forth—fourth	principal—principle	wood—would

Vocabulary in Context G3, SV 9780547625768

Homographs

Homographs are words that are spelled the same but have different meanings and different origins (*bat*—the mammal, *bat*—the club). Some homographs also have different pronunciations (*august*—majestic, *August*—eighth month).

close < shut / near

dove < pigeon / did dive

live < to exist / having life

desert < abandon / arid land

object < thing / disagree

record < to make note of / best achievement

tear < rip / drop of water from an eye

refuse < to say no / trash

lead < heavy metal / to be first

does < form of *do* / female deer

Prefixes

Prefixes are letter groups added before a base word to change or add to the word's meaning.

Prefix	Meaning	Example
auto-	self	autobiography
bi-	two	bicycle, biweekly
dis-	not	disbelief
im-	not	impossible
in-	into, not	inside, independence
non-	not	nonfiction
pre-	before	prehistoric
re-	again	resend
tele-	far	telescope
trans-	across	transportation
tri-	three	triangle
uni-	one	unify

Vocabulary in Context G3, SV 9780547625768

Suffixes

Suffixes are letter groups added after a base word to change or add to the word's meaning.

Suffix	Meaning	Example
-er	one who	teacher
-er	more	brighter
-est	most	brightest
-ful	full of	wonderful
-ing	(present tense)	smiling
-less	without	penniless
-ling	small	duckling
-ly	every	weekly
-ly	(adverb)	quickly
-ness	state of being	happiness
-or	one who	actor
-y	state of	funny

Vocabulary in Context G3, SV 9780547625768

The Age of the Dinosaur

Read the passage. Think about the meanings of the boldfaced words. Then go back to the passage. Underline the words or sentences that give you a clue to the meaning of each boldfaced word.

———————

Imagine Earth 220 million years ago. Much of the land had warm weather all year. Rain fell often in some places, so they were **moist**. The heat and wet air caused thick bushes, twisting vines, and tall trees to grow. In this **jungle** and across the open plains, some remarkable animals began to appear.

Dinosaurs were a group of four-legged animals that ruled Earth for about 140 million years. Some dinosaurs were as tall as a three-story building. Others were as small as cats.

No one has ever seen a dinosaur alive. Dinosaur footprints, bones, and teeth were **preserved**, or saved, in the ground. These **fossils** are often found in rocks. The rocks were once the mud in which dinosaurs walked.

Studying fossils gives us facts about dinosaurs. The shape of a dinosaur's teeth gives us **information** about whether it ate meat or plants. Its **skull** tells us what its head looked like. We know that many dinosaurs looked like huge **lizards**. They had long tails and scaly skin.

Why did dinosaurs disappear from Earth? Many people think that dinosaurs became **extinct** because Earth's weather changed. The **climate** may have cooled suddenly, killing the dinosaurs. The cause of this sudden change is unknown. However, we do know that dinosaurs were some of the most interesting animals ever to roam Earth.

Name _____ Date _____

Context Clues

Read each sentence. Look for clues to help you complete each sentence with a word from the box. Write the word on the line.

climate	dinosaurs	extinct	fossils	information
jungle	lizards	moist	preserved	skull

1. Many _____ were powerful beasts.

2. There are books that have _____ about what dinosaurs looked like and how they lived.

3. Dinosaur bones were _____ in mud that hardened into rocks.

4. We know from studying _____ that some dinosaurs had wings and could fly.

5. A _____ shows head size and shape.

6. The long tail of some dinosaurs was like the tail of some _____.

7. The dinosaurs walked in soft, _____ mud.

8. Some dinosaurs ate plants in the _____.

9. The _____, or weather, was hot.

10. When Earth's weather turned cold, the dinosaurs may have died and become _____.

Antonyms

Antonyms are words that have opposite meanings. Match the words in the box with their antonyms listed below. Write each word on the line.

| extinct | moist | preserved | jungle |

1. ruined _____

2. dry _____

3. living _____

4. desert _____

Dictionary Skills

A dictionary can help you find out how to say a word. Use the pronunciation key to help you learn how to say the vocabulary words in parentheses in the sentences below. Write the regular spelling for each word in parentheses.

Pronunciation Key				
i it	**u** up	ə **a** in ago	ī ice	**o** hot

1. The (skul) is made of bone. _____

2. The (liz´ərdz) climbed a tree. _____

3. We can learn from (fos´əlz). _____

4. The (klī´mit) got colder. _____

5. No one ever saw a (dī´nə sôr´). _____

Vocabulary in Context

Name _____ Date _____

Word Associations

Write the answer to each question. Use the words from the box.

climate	dinosaurs	extinct	fossils
jungle	lizards	moist	skull

1. Which word goes with *bone*? _____

2. Which word goes with *trees*? _____

3. Which word goes with *temperature*? _____

4. Which words go with *reptiles*? _____

5. Which word goes with *damp*? _____

6. Which word goes with *rocks*? _____

7. Which word goes with *gone*? _____

Writing Sentences

Use each vocabulary word in the box to write a sentence of your own.

climate	information	moist	preserved

1. _____

2. _____

3. _____

4. _____

Hidden Message Puzzle

Write a word from the box next to each clue. To find the message, copy the numbered letters in the matching numbered boxes at the bottom of the page. Then you will know something that dinosaurs left behind.

climate	preserved	extinct	skull
jungle	information	moist	

1. facts ☐☐☐☐☐☐☐☐☐☐☐
　　　　　1　　　　　　　　　　3

2. the weather in an area ☐☐☐☐☐☐☐
　　　　　　　　　　　　4

3. bone around the brain ☐☐☐☐☐
　　　　　10

4. hot place with thick plants ☐☐☐☐☐☐
　　　　　　　　　　8

5. damp ☐☐☐☐☐
　　　　2

6. saved ☐☐☐☐☐☐☐☐☐
　　　　5　　　　　6

7. no longer living on Earth ☐☐☐☐☐☐☐
　　　　　　　　　　　7　　　9

ANSWER: ☐☐☐☐☐☐☐☐☐☐
　　　　　1　2　3　4　5　6　7　8　9　10

Standardized Test Practice

Read each sentence. Pick the word that best completes the sentence. Circle the letter for the correct word.

TIP

Some tests have letters before the answer choices. Be sure to find the letter of the answer you think is correct and then circle the letter.

1. Powerful beasts called ____ lived long ago.

   A mice   **C** tails

   B dinosaurs   **D** lizards

2. Many books have ____ about dinosaurs.

   A paper   **C** information

   B skulls   **D** interest

3. Dinosaur bones were ____ in the ground.

   A preserved   **C** flying

   B grown   **D** cooled

4. The bones buried in rock and mud are called ____.

   A lizards   **C** fossils

   B climates   **D** jungles

5. Dinosaurs liked the warm air and thick plants in the ____.

   A fossils   **C** jungle

   B ocean   **D** desert

6. The jungle air was ____, or damp.

   A hot   **C** cold

   B moist   **D** blue

7. Some dinosaurs had a tail like ____.

   A fossils   **C** cats

   B skulls   **D** lizards

8. A dinosaur's ____ can show its head size.

   A skull   **C** feet

   B tail   **D** climate

Prefixes

A prefix comes at the beginning of a word and changes the meaning of the word. For example, *pre-* in *precaution* makes the word mean "care taken <u>before</u> something happens." Below are some prefixes and their meanings.

pre-	before	*un-*	not
re-	again	*over-*	too much

Read each word below. Write the meaning of the word. The first one is done for you.

1. prehistoric *before history* _____

2. overdo _____

3. untold _____

4. prepay _____

5. uncut _____

6. prejudge _____

7. rewrap _____

8. preheat _____

9. overuse _____

10. refilled _____

11. unwashed _____

12. overheat _____

Word Skills

Word Families

Cross out the word in each group that does not belong. Then add another word to each group. The first one is done for you.

1. prejudge   judged   ~~prepare~~   *judge* _____

2. wash   warm   washed _____

3. magnet   imagined   imagination _____

4. precaution   cautious   careful _____

5. clear   unclean   cleaning _____

6. reuse   redo   useful _____

7. sparkly   sparkling   parking _____

8. playground   underground   player _____

9. fill   film   refill _____

10. storage   prehistoric   historical _____

11. test   retest   precut _____

12. prepay   paying   pain _____

13. loading   lead   overload _____

14. preheat   heal   heated _____

15. hunter   hungrily   hungry _____

16. taste   tasty   tassle _____

Word Skills

    Vocabulary in Context G3, SV 9780547625768

Using Context

Read each sentence. Then write a definition for each underlined word.

1. That fossil is so old that it's <u>prehistoric</u>.

   _____

2. We will <u>prepay</u> for our tickets so we won't have to buy them when we get there.

   _____

3. Sue <u>preheated</u> the oven before she baked the cookies.

   _____

4. It isn't nice to <u>prejudge</u> people before you get to know them.

   _____

5. We brought an umbrella as a <u>precaution</u> in case it rains.

   _____

6. If you don't do it right, you will need to <u>redo</u> it.

   _____

7. Studying is one way to <u>prepare</u> for a test.

   _____

8. When my glass was empty, the waiter <u>refilled</u> it.

   _____

Word Skills

Name _____   Date _____

Writing

Some dinosaurs were quiet animals that ate plants. Others were mean and scary. Many even ate other dinosaurs. Look at the picture of the dinosaur on this page. Its name was Tyrannosaurus rex. Do you think it was friendly or fierce?

Use the lines below to describe this dinosaur.
Include how you think it moved, what it ate, and how it protected itself. Use some vocabulary words from this unit in your writing.

I think Tyrannosaurus rex was a _____

_____

_____

_____

_____

_____

_____

_____

Vocabulary in Context G3, SV 9780547625768

Writing

Mighty Paul Bunyan

Read the passage. Think about the meanings of the boldfaced words. Then go back to the passage. Underline the words or sentences that give you a clue to the meaning of each boldfaced word.

It is a dark night in the year 1895. Some men sit around a **campfire** watching the flames. These men are tired. They have worked hard all day chopping down trees in a forest. Now it is time for the storyteller to tell a story. The men listen as the story begins.

The **tale** is about a mighty man called Paul Bunyan. Paul is a lumberjack just like the men around the fire. He, too, chops down trees in the **wilderness**, far away from other people. But Paul Bunyan is not a real person. He is **imaginary**. He is bigger and stronger than real men and can do much more work. Paul Bunyan has the **ability** to clear a whole forest by himself! He eats more than real men do, too. It takes a whole **orchard** of trees to get enough apples to make him a pie!

Paul has a giant blue ox named Babe. Paul and Babe do many exciting things and have many **adventures**. For example, when Babe needs drinking water, Paul **scoops** out some big holes. These holes become the Great Lakes. Babe finally has enough water to drink!

How did these stories get started? What are their **beginnings**? The people who first told these tales took pride in their work as lumberjacks. This was their way of showing it. Over the years, these **legends** got passed along, and then were written down. Today, Paul Bunyan still stands for the kind of men and women who made our country strong.

Name _____ Date _PK 4 Wed_____

Context Clues

Read each sentence. Look for clues to help you complete each sentence with a word or words from the box. Write the word on the line.

campfire	scoops	imaginary	tale	ability
wilderness	beginnings	legends	orchard	adventures

1. Everyone outside was warmed by a _____.

2. They listened to a _____ told by a talented storyteller.

3. Paul Bunyan, an _____ person, lived in the _____ areas of the United States.

4. He had the _____ to chop down a whole _____ of trees at once.

5. In some of the stories, or _____, that people tell, Paul is helped by a blue ox named Babe.

6. In one of their exciting _____, Paul _____ out holes and makes the Great Lakes.

7. These stories had their _____ about a hundred years ago.

Challenge Yourself

1. Name two imaginary characters in books you have read.

_____

2. Name two adventures you have had with family or friends.

_____

Name _____ Date _____

Questions, Reasons, Examples

Answer the questions below. Use a dictionary if you need help.

1. How is a *legend* like a *tale*?

_____

2. Would you rather have a special *ability* or go on a special *adventure*? Why?

_____

3. What would you find in both an *orchard* and the *wilderness*?

_____

4. What would you do with a *campfire*?

_____

5. Does *adventures* or *scoops* mean "unusual experiences"?

_____

Writing Sentences

Use each vocabulary word in the box to write a sentence of your own.

beginnings	legends	imaginary
adventures	campfire	wilderness

1. _____

2. _____

3. _____

4. _____

5. _____

6. _____

Tangled-Up Words

A word is underlined in each sentence below. The word sounds something like a word in the box. But its meaning makes it the wrong word for the sentence.

Read the paragraphs. Find the word in the box that can replace the underlined word. Write the vocabulary word on the line next to the number of the underlined word.

Vocabulary in Context

adventures	legends	campfires	ability	tale
scoops	orchard	wilderness	imaginary	beginnings

Paul Bunyan is an (1) ordinary character. Storytellers often tell stories about him. These stories are told around (2) cameras. One (3) tail is about how much Paul can eat. It takes a whole (4) oranges of apples to make him a pie. Another story is about some holes he (5) scares out for Babe. They become the Great Lakes!

There are many other (6) ledges about Paul and his blue ox, Babe. Most tell about their different (7) alligators in the (8) windowsill.

People enjoy learning about the (9) buildings of a country through stories. Some people have a great (10) enemy to tell these stories well.

1. _____   6. _____

2. _____   7. _____

3. _____   8. _____

4. _____   9. _____

5. _____   10. _____

Vocabulary in Context

Dictionary Skills

Guide words are the two words at the top of each dictionary page. They show the first and last words on a page. All the words in between are in ABC order. Decide which words from the box would go on each page. Write the words in ABC order.

tale	beginnings	adventures	wilderness
scoops	campfire	orchard	ability

1. aardvark/day

_____

_____

_____

_____

2. nose/yellow

_____

_____

_____

_____

Synonyms

Synonyms are words that have the same or almost the same meaning. Match the words in the box with their synonyms listed below. Write each word from the box on the line.

scoops	ability	legends	imaginary

1. stories _____

2. digs _____

3. pretend _____

4. skill _____

Name _____ Date _____

Standardized Test Practice

Read each sentence. Pick the word that best completes the sentence. Circle the letter for the correct word.

> **TIP**
> If you are not sure which word completes the sentence, do the best you can. Try to choose the answer that makes the most sense.

1. A **tale** is a kind of ____.

   A story   C dog

   B character   D poem

2. A **campfire** is built in the ____.

   A stove   C woods

   B vans   D lake

3. A person who **scoops** out dirt ____ it out.

   A digs   C fills

   B washes   D blows

4. A **wilderness** is a ____ place.

   A tasty   C space

   B city   D wild

5. An **imaginary** story is ____.

   A true   C old

   B not real   D very short

6. Someone with **ability** has ____.

   A instruments   C charm

   B skill   D wrinkles

7. An **orchard** has many ____.

   A children   C trees

   B animals   D rooms

8. **Adventures** are ____.

   A exciting   C proud

   B dull   D messy

9. **Beginnings** are how something was ____.

   A written   C won

   B finished   D started

10. **Legends** are well-known ____ about the past.

    A recipes   C heroes

    B stories   D accidents

Vocabulary in Context G3, SV 9780547625768

Name _____ Date _____

Explore Word Meaning

Read and respond to each of the following questions or statements.

1. What books or stories have you read that are *fantasies*?

_____

2. Would you rather read a story about *real* people or *imaginary* people?

_____

3. What are some things that could happen in a *yarn* that couldn't happen in a true story?

_____

4. What other characters might you read about in a *tale* about a princess?

_____

5. Pretend you are writing a *fantasy* story. Draw a picture of the main character in your story. Then name your character.

_____

Unit 2
Vocabulary in Context G3, SV 9780547625768

Word Skills

Using the Dictionary

Entry words in a dictionary are listed in alphabetical order. An entry word in a dictionary is followed by its pronunciation. Its part of speech is next. If there are two meanings, they are each numbered. Dictionaries sometimes include an example sentence to explain the meaning of the word.

Read the entries below. Then answer the questions.

imaginary [i maj´ə ner ē] *adj.* Existing only in the imagination, unreal.

pretend [pri tend´] *v.* To make believe: *Let's pretend we're movie stars.*

yarn [yarn] *n.* **1.** Any spun strand. **2.** A made-up story.

1. How many syllables are in *imaginary*?

_____

2. Is a *yarn* a true story? How do you know?

_____

3. Why are there numerals in the meaning of *yarn*?

_____

4. Make up a new example sentence for *pretend*.

_____

5. Which word is pronounced this way? [i maj´ə ner ē]

_____

6. Why is *yarn* the last word listed here?

_____

Word Skills

Name _____ Date <u>Pk 7 Wed</u>

Homophones

The words in each homophone pair below are pronounced the same but have different spellings and different meanings. Write the word from the box that matches each clue below.

| pear–pair   stare–stair   our–hour |

Which word means…

1. belongs to us? _____

2. sixty minutes? _____

3. a fruit? _____

4. two of something? _____

5. something you climb? _____

6. to look at? _____

Now try these.

| tale–tail   whole–hole |

Which word means…

7. what you dig? _____

8. all of something? _____

9. what a dog wags? _____

10. a story? _____

Unit 2
Vocabulary in Context G3, SV 9780547625768

Word Skills

Writing

Pretend you are Paul Bunyan. You've just met a woman twice as big and much stronger than you are.

Describe the new character and tell how you feel about her. Use some vocabulary words from this unit in your writing.

I was walking through the forest when, to my surprise, I saw _____

_____

_____

_____

_____

_____

_____

_____

_____

_____

_____

Writing

Reading

Tell Me a Story

Read the passage. Think about the meanings of the boldfaced words. Then go back to the passage. Underline the words or sentences that give you a clue to the meaning of each boldfaced word.

Many people tell stories just for fun. Did you know that some people make money by telling stories? These **professional** storytellers know how to hold people's attention and make them smile. They tour the country to **entertain** people in many different places.

You may have seen a storyteller at work. Some storytellers dress in a **costume** and use music to help tell a story. Seeing such a performer is a special **event**, and the storyteller wants you to enjoy it.

Author Patricia McKissack is a professional storyteller. She travels to schools and other public places to tell stories to children and adults. McKissack tells stories with power and excitement. The **energy** that she puts into her stories makes her a popular performer.

As she tells a tale, McKissack often describes a silly, **comic** character. Then the listeners burst out with **laughter** at the funny person. Just as quickly, the **audience** listens **intently** as they hear about a character in trouble. Nothing takes their attention away from the story McKissack is telling.

Then the monkey jumped off the table and hid under the tablecloth.

People have been telling stories for thousands of years. Patricia McKissack and others like her are helping to keep the **ancient** art of storytelling alive. These storytellers are popular because everyone loves to hear a good story. So tell me a story!

Context Clues

Meanings for the vocabulary words are given below. Go back to the passage and read each sentence that has a vocabulary word. If you still cannot tell the meaning, look for clues in the sentences that come before and after the one with the vocabulary word. Write each word from the box in front of its meaning.

ancient	entertain	energy	comic	professional
audience	intently	costume	laughter	event

1. _____ to hold people's interest

2. _____ very old

3. _____ the power to work and act

4. _____ people watching a show

5. _____ a happening

6. _____ funny

7. _____ a special set of clothes

8. _____ making money by doing something that others do for fun

9. _____ with close attention

10. _____ the sound of laughing

Challenge Yourself

Name two <u>comic</u> actors.

Understanding Multiple-Meaning Words

The words in the boxes have more than one meaning. Look for clues in each sentence to tell which meaning is used. Write the letter of the meaning next to the correct sentence.

Vocabulary in Context

comic **a.** a person who tells jokes; **b.** funny

1. ____   It is a comic play.

2. ____   We laughed at the comic.

entertain **a.** to hold people's attention; **b.** to have as a guest

3. ____   The story will entertain us.

4. ____   We can entertain friends at home.

Cloze Paragraph

Use the words in the box to complete the paragraph. Reread the paragraph to be sure it makes sense.

audience   laughter   entertain   event   costume

Next month we will put on a play. It is a yearly _____
(1)

that everyone enjoys. My sister is making me a _____ to
(2)

wear. I can't wait to _____ all the people who will be in
(3)

the _____. Our play is funny, and we want to hear their
(4)

_____.
(5)

Word Associations

Write an answer to each question.

1. When might you wear a *costume* to *entertain*?

_____

_____

2. When might an *audience* break out in *laughter*?

_____

_____

3. Where might you see a *professional comic*?

_____

_____

4. What *ancient event* do we still talk about today?

_____

_____

5. How can you tell that an *audience* is high *energy*?

_____

_____

6. What is one thing you have done *intently* today?

_____

_____

www.harcourtschoolsupply.com
© HMH Supplemental Publishers Inc. All rights reserved.

Unit 3
Vocabulary in Context G3, SV 9780547625768

Vocabulary in Context

Crossword Puzzle

Use the clues and the words in the box to finish the crossword puzzle.

ancient	costume	event	professional	audience
energy	intently	comic	entertain	laughter

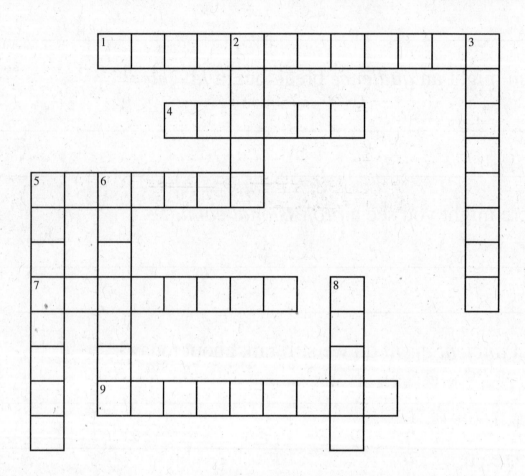

Across

1. expert

4. power to do work

5. very old

7. with great interest

9. what storytellers do

Down

2. a happening

3. sound of ha, ha, ha

5. people who listen or watch

6. special clothes for an actor or storyteller

8. funny

Unit 3
Vocabulary in Context G3, SV 9780547625768

Vocabulary in Context

Standardized Test Practice

Read each sentence. Pick the word that best completes the sentence. Circle the letter for the correct word.

> **TIP**
> Read carefully. Use the other words in the sentences to help you choose each missing word.

1. Carlo is paid to write stories. He is a ____ writer.

   A lonely   C lazy

   B private   D professional

2. Anne was dressed to look like a princess. Everyone loved her ____.

   A smile   C dog

   B costume   D lamp

3. The contest is today. We will go to see this special ____.

   A audience   C energy

   B event   D fish

4. I wanted to learn the words to the song. I listened very ____.

   A intently   C sadly

   B cautiously   D sleepily

5. The museum has very old works of art. I saw an ____ vase.

   A up-to-date   C ancient

   B invisible   D improved

6. That story made me laugh. It is a ____ tale.

   A sad   C comic

   B professional   D helpful

7. We clapped at the end of the show. We were a happy ____.

   A act   C address

   B audience   D aunt

8. Tran told a funny joke. We roared with ____.

   A anger   C tears

   B fear   D laughter

Name _____ Date _____

Classify/Categorize

Read each group of words below. Circle the letter of the word that does not belong in each group. Then add a category name for each group. The first one has been done for you.

1. A carpenter
   B mason
   C storyteller
   D builder
   people who build things

2. A hammer
   B saw
   C screwdriver
   D house
   _____

3. A brick
   B candle
   C wood
   D steel
   _____

4. A apple
   B banana
   C green bean
   D grape
   _____

5. A jungle gym
   B slide
   C swings
   D tomato
   _____

6. A chair
   B toast
   C cereal
   D pancakes
   _____

7. A electrician
   B plumber
   C wood
   D machinist
   _____

8. A fruit punch
   B window
   C orange juice
   D milk
   _____

9. A crayon
   B pen
   C pencil
   D tree
   _____

10. A quarter
    B dime
    C fan
    D nickel
    _____

Name _____   Date _____

Analogies

In an analogy, two pairs of words go together in the same way.

Examples:

> The sun shines in the day. The moon shines at night.
> *Sun* is to *day* as *moon* is to *night*.

Choose a word from the box to complete each analogy.

flowers   watch   wood   pipes   trees

1. A mason works with bricks. A carpenter works with _____.

2. Apples are fruit. Roses are _____.

3. A beach has sand. A forest has _____.

4. An electrician fixes electrical wiring. A plumber fixes water _____.

5. A book is something you read. A television set is something you _____.

Now try these.

wear   machines   sour   short

6. *Storytellers* are to *stories* as *machinists* are to _____.

7. *Hot* is to *cold* as *tall* is to _____.

8. *Food* is to *eat* as *costumes* are to _____.

9. *Sugar* is to *sweet* as *lemon* is to _____.

Vocabulary in Context G3, SV 9780547625768

Word Skills

Name _____ Date _____

Compare and Contrast

Complete the following statements.

1. A *carpenter* is like a *mason* except _____

_____.

2. *Wood* is like *brick* because _____

_____.

3. A *plumber* is like an *electrician* except _____

_____.

4. *Ancient* is like *prehistoric* because _____

_____.

5. A *fork* is like a *spoon* because _____

_____.

6. A *cabin* is like a *mansion* except _____

_____.

7. A *piano* is like a *flute* because _____

_____.

8. A *lake* is like an *ocean* except _____

_____.

9. A *quarter* is like a *dime* except _____

_____.

Name _____ Date _____

Writing

Storytellers tell different kinds of stories. They retell some old favorites. Sometimes they make up new stories.

Write a story you like. It can be an old favorite or a new one. Use some vocabulary words from this unit in your writing.

_____

_____

_____

_____

_____

_____

_____

_____

_____

Writing

A World Below the Trees

Read the passage. Think about the meanings of the boldfaced words. Then go back to the passage. Underline the words or sentences that give you a clue to the meaning of each boldfaced word.

You are walking near the edge of a tropical rain forest. The jungle plants are so **thick**, so close together, that you must slowly push your way through. Then the jungle ends, and you enter the rain forest itself. Here the **distance**, or space, between the plants is greater.

A tropical rain forest is made up of different **levels**. The top level is a ceiling of treetops. Measured from the ground up, the treetops reach 100 to 200 feet in **height**. The middle level is made up of shorter trees and bushes. Here, many animals and insects live. The number of different kinds of insects alone is well over one **thousand**. Plants at the lowest level, the forest floor, are about a **meter** high, or just over 39 inches.

Jungles often grow at the edge of rain forests. But if you **compare** the two, you see that they are not alike. Many plants crowd the sunny jungle. Plants are not as **numerous** on the rain forest floor since it is shaded by the treetops.

Today, rain forests are changing. People cut down trees and use the land to grow crops. As people **increase** their use of the land, rain forests get smaller.

We must try to protect these rain forests. Not only are they home to many animals and plants, but they also help **supply** Earth with oxygen. Rain forests give us clean air to breathe.

Vocabulary in Context G3, SV 9780547625768

Context Clues

Meanings for the vocabulary words are given below. Go back to
the passage and read each sentence that has a vocabulary word.
If you still cannot tell the meaning, look for clues in the sentences
that come before and after the one with the vocabulary word. Write
each word from the box in front of its meaning.

thick	increase	compare	distance	meter
thousand	supply	numerous	height	levels

1. _____ : many

2. _____ : how tall something is

3. _____ : to get larger in amount or size

4. _____ : a measure

5. _____ : the number word for 1,000

6. _____ : to give something needed

7. _____ : how far it is between things; space

8. _____ : to see how things are alike

9. _____ : having things close together

10. _____ : measures of height

Challenge Yourself

1. Name two things you might measure in <u>meters</u>.

_____

2. Name two things you might <u>compare</u>.

_____

Vocabulary in Context

Synonyms

Remember that synonyms are words that have the same or almost the same meaning. Write a word from the box that is a synonym of the underlined word in each sentence.

numerous	levels	supply	increases

1. When a tree <u>grows</u>, it _____ in size.

2. So <u>many</u> trees and plants are in a rain forest that they are too _____ to count.

3. Rain forests <u>give</u> animals a place to live and help _____ Earth with oxygen.

4. There are three <u>stages</u>, or _____, in a rain forest.

Writing Sentences

Use each vocabulary word in the box to write a sentence of your own.

distance	height	thick
thousand	compare	meter

1. _____

2. _____

3. _____

4. _____

5. _____

6. _____

Word Game

Write a word from the box next to each clue. Then read the words formed by the boxed letters. They name animals that live in the rain forest.

thick	thousand	distance	meter	levels
increase	supply	compare	height	numerous

Vocabulary in Context

1. a measure ☐ ___ ___ ___ ___

2. see what is alike ___ ___ ___ ___ ☐ ___ ___

3. many of something ☐ ___ ___ ___ ___ ___ ___ ___

4. to give ___ ___ ___ ___ ☐ ___

5. a large number ___ ___ ___ ☐ ___ ___ ___ ___

6. become greater in size ___ ☐ ___ ___ ___ ___ ___ ___

7. how far to go ___ ___ ___ ☐ ___ ___ ___ ___

8. not thin ___ ___ ___ ☐ ___

9. how high ___ ☐ ___ ___ ___ ___

10. stages ___ ___ ___ ___ ___ ☐

Name _____ Date _____

Word Webs

Complete word webs for the three vocabulary words. Think of words that mean the same as, or somehow relate to, the center word.

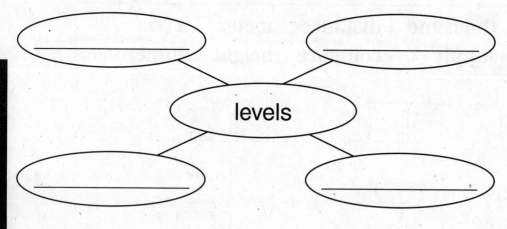

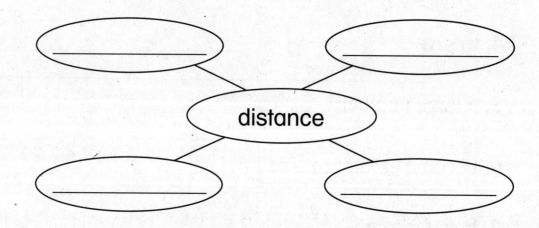

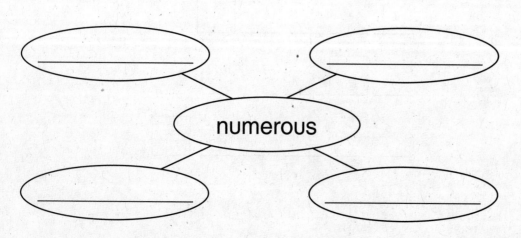

Standardized Test Practice

Find the word or words that mean the same or about the same as the boldfaced word. Circle the letter for the correct answer.

TIP
This test will show how well you understand the meaning of each word. Think about the meaning of the **boldfaced** word before you choose your answer.

Vocabulary in Context

1. a **meter** long
   A a measure
   B an amount of time
   C a year
   D a pound

2. **increase** the amount
   A continue   C make greater
   B bring down D enjoy

3. the **thick** forest
   A crowded together
   B thinly placed
   C strange
   D rich

4. **supply** food
   A spoil   C look at
   B throw out D give

5. all the **levels**
   A stars   C stages
   B colors   D letters

6. **numerous** people
   A some   C none
   B many   D few

7. the tree's **height**
   A leaves   C how tall
   B coloring D how heavy

8. **distance** between
   A object   C person
   B space   D dirt

9. **compare** things
   A see how alike
   B complete
   C join
   D leave behind

10. reached a **thousand**
    A large number
    B large building
    C small child
    D small animal

Name _____ Date _____

Classify/Categorize

Write each word from the box under the correct category. Then write your own word for each category.

| computers | relationships | habitat | snakes | environment |
| alligators | reptiles | | software | microchips |

---

1. herpetology

_____

_____

_____

2. ecology

_____

_____

_____

3. technology

_____

_____

_____

| ancient cities | mammals | flowers |
| trees | culture | ruins |

---

4. biology

_____

_____

_____

5. archaeology

_____

_____

_____

Name _____ Date _____

Dictionary Skills

Use the dictionary entry below to answer the following questions.

e•col•o•gy [ē kol´ə jē] *n.* **1.** The study of how living things relate to their surroundings. **2.** The balance between living things and their surroundings. —ecologist, *n.*

1. Which of these shows the correct syllable to stress in *ecology*? Circle the letter of the correct answer.

   A [ē kol ə´jē]

   B [ē´kol ə jē]

   C [ē kol´ə jē]

   D [ē kol ə jē´]

2. How many meanings does *ecology* have? _____

3. What part of speech is *ecology*? _____

4. What word is based on *ecology* in the dictionary entry?

   _____

5. If the suffix *-ist* means "a person," what do you think *ecologist* means?

   _____

6. Write a sentence using *ecology*.

   _____

7. Write a sentence using *ecologist*.

   _____

Word Skills

Word Parts

Add the root and the suffix together to create a word. Then use the meaning of each word part to write a definition for the word.

Suffixes		Roots	
-logy	the study of	*archaeo*	ancient
-ist	a person who makes or studies	*bio*	living things
		chrono	time
		eco	environment
		herpeto	reptiles
		psycho	mind

1. eco + *-logy* = _____

2. bio + *-logy* = _____

3. archaeo + *-logy* = _____

4. herpeto + *-logy* = _____

5. chrono + *-logy* − *-y* + *-ist* = _____

6. psycho + *-logy* − *-y* + *-ist* = _____

7. What are some other *-logy* or *-ist* words? _____

_____

Unit 4
Vocabulary in Context G3, SV 9780547625768

Writing

   Imagine you are on a trip through a rain forest. You can take only three pictures of what you see.

On the lines below, describe each picture you would take. Tell about the plants, animals, or insects in it. Use some vocabulary words from this unit in your writing.

Picture 1

_____

_____

_____

_____

Picture 2

_____

_____

_____

_____

Picture 3

_____

_____

_____

_____

Writing

The Spinning Star

Read the passage. Think about the meanings of the boldfaced words. Then go back to the passage. Underline the words or sentences that give you a clue to the meaning of each boldfaced word.

The lights go down. Heads look up. At the top of the tent a woman spins around on metal loops attached to ropes. The **performer** is Lillian Leitzel, a circus star.

In her time (1891–1931), Leitzel was one of the world's most famous circus performers. She had a very **difficult** act, but she made it look easy. Leitzel had **confidence** in her skills. She believed in what she could do, and so did her fans.

To begin her act, Leitzel went up a long rope that hung from the top of the tent. Her trip up the rope was done in a series of smooth, **graceful** movements. She spun by swinging from hand to hand and turning her body over each time she changed hands. To do this, Leitzel had to be very strong and in good **condition**. The big **muscles** in her arms and shoulders helped.

At the top of the rope, far above the crowd, Lillian Leitzel did handstands and other **balancing** tricks. Then came the hardest part, her biggest **challenge**. She held onto a metal ring with one hand. Then she swung her body up and over the ring again and again. Leitzel did this **exhausting** trick at least 75 times a show. Only an **athlete** in top condition could do this.

In 1931, a ring Leitzel was using broke during one of her acts. She fell to her death. It was a great loss to the circus world. But Lillian Leitzel will always be remembered for her bravery and skill.

Name _____ Date _____

Context Clues

Read each sentence. Look for clues to help you complete each sentence with a word or words from the box. Write the correct word on the line.

confidence	challenge	graceful	balancing	performer
muscles	difficult	exhausting	condition	athlete

1. Like a swimmer, runner, or other _____, Lillian Leitzel practiced a lot.

2. Practice helped her learn _____ tricks, like

   _____ on a rope.

3. She also exercised to stay in good _____.

4. Leitzel needed strong arm _____.

5. Her movements had to be smooth and _____.

6. She also needed _____, or belief, in herself.

7. For Lillian Leitzel, doing hard tricks was a _____.

8. The life of a circus _____ was exciting.

9. But the long days of tiring work were also _____.

Vocabulary in Context

Vocabulary in Context G3, SV 9780547625768

Name _____   Date _____

Synonyms

Remember that synonyms are words that have the same or almost the same meaning. Match the words in the box with their synonyms. Write each word on the line.

difficult   athlete   exhausting   confidence

1. tiring _____

2. trust _____

3. hard _____

4. runner _____

Glossary Skills

A glossary gives the meanings of words. Turn to the Glossary, which begins on page 108. Find each word in the Glossary. Write its meaning below.

1. graceful: _____

2. challenge: _____

3. performer: _____

4. balancing: _____

5. condition: _____

6. muscles: _____

7. confidence: _____

8. exhausting: _____

Vocabulary in Context (side tab)

50

Word Map

Words can be put on a kind of map to show what they have in common. Write each word from the box in the group where it belongs to tell about Lillian Leitzel.

confidence	challenges	graceful	balancing	performer
muscles	difficult	exhausting	condition	athlete

What She Is

a _____

an _____

What She Has

body _____

_____ in herself

LILLIAN LEITZEL

What She Faces

big _____

_____ work

**What Kind of Tricks
She Does**

_____ tricks

_____ acts

What She Has to Be

very _____

in good _____

Name _____ Date _____

Adding -ing

An -ing ending is added to a verb to describe an action that is or was happening at a certain time.

hire + -ing = hiring   gasp + -ing = gasping

Add -ing to each root word. Write a sentence using each word.

1. balance _____

_____

2. exhaust _____

_____

Questions, Reasons, Examples

Answer the following questions. Use a dictionary if you need help.

1. What could you do to make your *muscles* ache?

_____

2. What activity gives your mind a *challenge*?

_____

3. What might an *athlete* do after school?

_____

4. What activity would a *graceful* person be good at?

_____

5. What would it look like to walk into a room with *confidence*?

_____

Vocabulary in Context

Standardized Test Practice

Read each sentence. Pick the word that best completes the sentence. Circle the letter for the correct word.

TIP

> Before you choose an answer, try reading the sentence with each answer choice. This will help you choose an answer that makes sense.

1. A circus _____ appears in front of many people.

   A play   **C** performer

   B business   **D** dinosaur

2. A _____ act takes skill.

   A prehistoric   **C** balancing

   B narrow   **D** noisy

3. This circus work is _____.

   A round   **C** gentle

   B difficult   **D** rainy

4. She has strong _____.

   A muscles   **C** athlete

   B advertisements **D** lizards

5. Watch her _____ movements.

   A loud   **C** graceful

   B orange   **D** mouthful

6. I have had an _____ day.

   A extinct   **C** exhausting

   B equal   **D** entertain

7. We have _____ in you.

   A canvas   **C** climate

   B confidence   **D** carpenter

8. You are in good _____.

   A condition   **C** muscles

   B yarns   **D** precaution

9. Here is our star _____.

   A audience   **C** athlete

   B business   **D** energy

10. Spinning is a big _____.

    A laughter   **C** information

    B slogan   **D** challenge

Colorful Words

Colorful words make writing more interesting. Read each sentence part and its word choices. Write the most colorful word to complete each sentence part.

1. the _____ necklace

   pretty   sparkling

2. the _____ bunny

   fluffy   soft

3. the _____ star

   twinkling   bright

4. the _____ elephant

   big   enormous

5. the _____ candle

   glimmering   nice

6. the _____ snail

   slow   sluggish

7. the _____ water

   shimmering   pretty

8. the _____ jewel

   glistening   shiny

9. the _____ bear

   mean   fierce

10. the _____ ice-cream cone

   good   delicious

Unit 5
Vocabulary in Context G3, SV 9780547625768

Word Skills

Word Endings

Complete the word puzzles. Add the endings *-s*, *-ed*, and *-ing* to each word.

1. sparkle

__ __ __ __ __ __ __ __ __

__ __ __ __ __ __ __ __ __

__ __ __ __ __ __ __ __ __

2. twinkle

__ __ __ __ __ __ __ __ __

__ __ __ __ __ __ __ __ __

__ __ __ __ __ __ __ __ __

3. glimmer

__ __ __ __ __ __ __ __ __

__ __ __ __ __ __ __ __ __

__ __ __ __ __ __ __ __ __

4. glisten

__ __ __ __ __ __ __ __ __

__ __ __ __ __ __ __ __ __

__ __ __ __ __ __ __ __ __

Word Skills

Vocabulary in Context G3, SV 9780547625768

Compare and Contrast

The words *glare* and *shimmer* are alike in some ways and different in others. Look at the diagram below. In the center circle, write the word from the box that tells about both words. In the circle with *glare*, write the five words that tell only about *glare*. In the circle with *shimmer*, write the six words that tell only about *shimmer*.

harsh	gentle	soft	fierce
burn	glistening	sparkling	shine
bright	twinkling	uncomfortable	glimmering

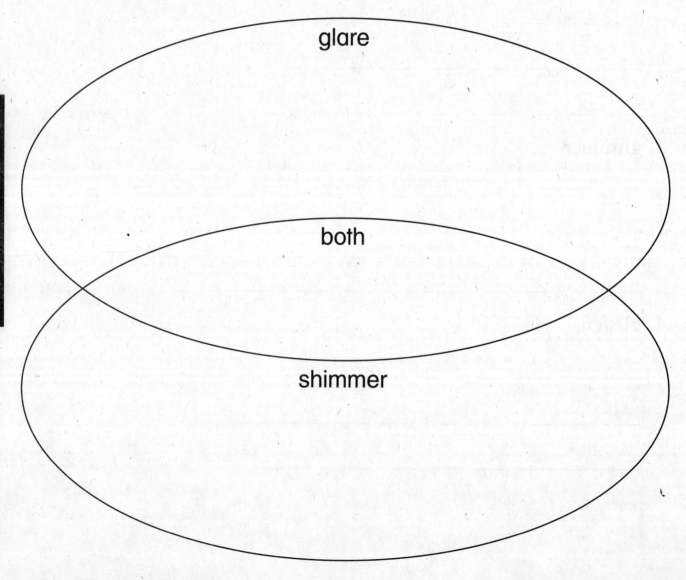

glare

both

shimmer

Word Skills

Name _____ Date _____

Writing

When a circus comes to town, it puts up ads to get people to come to the show. Each advertisement describes the acts and performers. Imagine that you have a circus. Your circus has different kinds of performers and animals.

Write your own advertisement. Tell why your circus is the best circus and why people should buy a ticket to see it. Use some vocabulary words from this unit in your writing.

CIRCUS

Come one, come all, to the greatest circus on Earth! You will see _____

_____

_____

_____

_____

_____

_____

_____

Vocabulary in Context G3, SV 9780547625768

Writing

The Mickey Mouse Man

Read the passage. Think about the meanings of the boldfaced words. Then go back to the passage. Underline the words or sentences that give you a clue to the meaning of each boldfaced word.

Have you ever been to Disney World or to Disneyland? If you have, then you know who Walt Disney was. He made his living in the **entertainment** business. Or, you could say his **career** was amusing people. One way Disney did this was by inventing animal **characters** such as Mickey Mouse and Donald Duck.

When he was a boy, Walt Disney liked to draw. At the age of 16, he began to study art in Chicago, Illinois. His **drawings** showed that he was a good artist. He had **talent**.

Six years later, Disney moved to California to make **cartoons**. A cartoon is a movie made from thousands of drawings. Each one shows a small part of the character's actions.

Disney set up a **studio** so he would have a place to make his movies. His first cartoon was about Mickey Mouse. People were **delighted** with Mickey Mouse. They loved his big ears and were **enchanted** with his squeaky voice. (They did not know it was really Walt Disney's own charming voice!)

Walt Disney went on to make many other cartoons. People liked the **humor** in Disney's cartoons. The stories were funny, and the characters did silly things.

Today, the Disney Studios still carry on Walt Disney's work. Mickey Mouse and the other Disney characters still make people laugh.

Context Clues

Meanings for the vocabulary words are given below. Go back to the passage and read each sentence that has a vocabulary word. If you still cannot tell the meaning, look for clues in the sentences that come before and after the one with the vocabulary word. Write each word from the box in front of its meaning.

characters	career	drawings	talent	entertainment
studio	delighted	humor	cartoons	enchanted

1. _____ : a person's life work

2. _____ : place where an artist might work

3. _____ : pictures done with pencil, pen, or crayon

4. _____ : very pleased and happy

5. _____ : something that keeps people interested

6. _____ : movies made from many pictures

7. _____ : greatly charmed

8. _____ : people and animals in a story

9. _____ : what makes someone laugh

10. _____ : special ability

Unit 6
Vocabulary in Context G3, SV 9780547625768

Vocabulary in Context

Cloze Paragraph

Use the words in the box to complete the paragraph. Reread the paragraph to be sure it makes sense.

cartoons	entertainment	talent
delighted	characters	studio

Walt Disney had great (1) _____. He created several

famous cartoon (2) _____. Mickey and Donald

(3) _____ people everywhere. (4) _____

showing the silly animals made people laugh. Walt Disney's

(5) _____ grew and made more movies. Disney World

and Disneyland provided new kinds of (6) _____.

Writing Sentences

Use each vocabulary word in the box to write a sentence of your own.

enchanted	career	drawings	humor

1. _____

2. _____

3. _____

4. _____

Word Groups

Read each pair of words. Think about how they are alike. Write the word from the box that best completes each word group.

talent   career   delighted   drawings

1. job, work, _____

2. paintings, sculptures, _____

3. skill, ability, _____

4. pleased, thrilled, _____

Dictionary Skills

Remember that guide words are the two words at the top of each dictionary page. They show the first and last words on a page. All the words in between are in ABC order. Decide which words from the box would go on each page. Write the words in ABC order.

| characters   cartoons   entertainment |
career   enchanted humor

1. bug/edge   **2.** elephant/ice

_____   _____

_____   _____

_____   _____

Name _____   Date _____

Word Map

Words can be put on a word map to show what they have in common. Write each word from the box in the group where it belongs to tell about Walt Disney.

delighted	characters	talent	entertainment	cartoons
enchanted	studio	humor	drawings	

What He Created Himself

_____

_____

_____

How He Made People Feel

_____

_____

WALT DISNEY

What Helped Him Succeed

sense of _____

_____

Where He Worked

_____ business

his own _____

Name _____ Date _____

Standardized Test Practice

Read the phrase. Look for the word or words that have the same or almost the same meaning as the boldfaced word. Circle the letter for the correct answer.

TIP
Always read all the answer choices. Many choices may make sense. But only one answer choice has the same or almost the same meaning as the **boldfaced** word.

1. Disney **cartoons**
   A car tools   C coats
   B plays   D movies

2. person's **career**
   A life's work   C drawings
   B last name   D hobby

3. Disney **characters**
   A actions
   B charms
   C animals or people
   D candies or treats

4. artist's **studio**
   A student
   B brush
   C good idea
   D place of work

5. box of **drawings**
   A books   C pictures
   B letters   D paints

6. with **humor**
   A love   C hate
   B fun   D tears

7. good **entertainment**
   A creepy thing
   B empty thing
   C boring thing
   D interesting thing

8. having **talent**
   A ability   C beauty
   B attention   D business

9. become **enchanted**
   A cheerful   C surprised
   B charmed   D eaten

10. feel **delighted**
    A unhappy   C curious
    B pleased   D deserted

Vocabulary in Context G3, SV 9780547625768

Name _____ Date _____

Related Words

Every type of career has jobs that are related to it. Underneath each category, draw a picture that represents it. Then write each job from the word box underneath the type of career it is related to. Finally, add a job to each list.

paramedic	paralegal	referee	coach
doctor	singer	trainer	lawyer
legal secretary	actress	comedian	nurse
actor	surgeon	basketball player	

1. Athletic Careers	2. Medical Careers	3. Legal Careers	4. Entertainment Careers
_____	_____	_____	_____
_____	_____	_____	_____
_____	_____	_____	_____
_____	_____	_____	_____

Word Skills

Name _____ Date _____

Explore Word Meaning

Read and respond to each question. Use complete sentences.

1. What are some special skills that people with careers in athletics need to have?

_____

_____

2. What kind of personality do you think you would need if you wanted a legal career?

_____

_____

3. When might you need to see someone who has a medical career?

_____

_____

4. There are many different entertainment careers. In what type of entertainment career would you be most interested? Why?

_____

_____

Rank the types of careers from one to four. Your number-one career should be the one in which you are most interested. Your number-four career should be the one in which you are least interested. Then explain the reason for your order.

_____ athletic   _____ legal

_____ entertainment   _____ medical

_____

_____

Vocabulary in Context G3, SV 9780547625768

Word Skills

Word Families

The word *career* is based on a word that means "car." All the words in the box are in the same family because they come from this word. Read the words and their meanings. Then use each word to complete one of the sentences. You will use one word twice.

car	a vehicle that takes you places
career	work that takes you through life
carriage	a fancy kind of wagon pulled by a horse
carry	to move something from one place to another
chariots	carts with two wheels, pulled by horses; used long ago in races

1. My uncle has a _____ in agriculture.

2. We drove to Florida in our _____.

3. The ancient Romans raced each other in their _____.

4. A horse pulled our _____ in a ride around the park.

5. You are too heavy for me to _____.

6. My sister has a _____ in medicine.

Use two of the words in the list above in sentences of your own.

7. _____

_____

8. _____

_____

Word Skills

Writing

Pretend you have been asked to create a brand-new cartoon character for a movie. Write a paragraph describing your character. What is its name? How does it look? Use some vocabulary words from this unit in your writing.

_____

_____

_____

_____

_____

_____

_____

_____

_____

_____

Writing

Vocabulary in Context G3, SV 9780547625768

Computer Cartoons

Read the passage. Think about the meanings of the boldfaced words. Then go back to the passage. Underline the words or sentences that give you a clue to the meaning of each boldfaced word.

When you turn on your **television** set, you can almost always find a cartoon. The cartoon may be a show like Bugs Bunny. Or it may be a **commercial** to help sell a toy. You can even see whole movies that are cartoons. They are fun for us to watch. But for many years, **creating** cartoons was hard work. To make cartoons, artists had to draw **countless** pictures by hand. Then the artists had to **arrange** the thousands of pictures from the beginning of the cartoon to the end.

Today, computers are making the job of cartoon artists much easier. First, the artists use the computer to draw the shape of an object or person. This **figure** looks like a wire sculpture. The computer lets the artists look at the figure from any direction–front, back, top, or bottom. The artists use the keyboard or mouse to turn the figure and make it move. The artists then **develop** the figure. For example, they add face details such as hair, a nose, mouth, and eyes. They also add clothes to the figure.

To show a **motion** such as skipping, computer artists only have to draw pictures of the figure at the beginning, middle, and end of the movement. The computer then fills in the **images** in between because it has a record of how the figure looks when it moves. The **effect** is smooth movement that looks real and a cartoon character that is a modern work of art.

Name _____ Date _____

Context Clues

Meanings for the vocabulary words are given below. Go back to the passage and read each sentence that has a vocabulary word. If you still cannot tell the meaning, look for clues in the sentences that come before and after the one with the vocabulary word. Write each word from the box in front of its meaning.

figure	countless	develop	motion	television
creating	images	commercial	arrange	effect

1. _____ : likenesses of people, animals, or things

2. _____ : to work out in detail

3. _____ : a machine that shows pictures with sounds

4. _____ : the act of moving

5. _____ : an ad on the radio or television

6. _____ : too many to be counted

7. _____ : to put in some kind of order

8. _____ : a shape

9. _____ : the act of making something new

10. _____ : the result

69
Unit 7
Vocabulary in Context G3, SV 9780547625768

Cloze Paragraph

Use the words in the box to complete the paragraph. Reread the paragraph to be sure it makes sense.

countless	television	creating	commercial

Last night I turned on the _____'_____ set. I was looking for
(1)

a cartoon to watch. As I flipped through the channels, I saw a great

_____. It was an ad for the new science museum. An
(2)

artist had painted _____ pictures of insects all over the
(3)

walls of the museum. I'll bet that _____ all those pictures
(4)

took her months!

Understanding Multiple-Meaning Words

The words in the box have more than one meaning. Look for clues in each sentence to tell which meaning is being used. Write the letter of the meaning next to the correct sentence.

develop	figures
a. to work out in detail	**a.** numbers
b. to make bigger or better	**b.** shapes

_____ **1.** Exercise helped him <u>develop</u> his muscles.

_____ **2.** We added the <u>figures</u> in the math problem.

Vocabulary in Context

Dictionary Skills

Remember that guide words are the two words at the top of each dictionary page. They show the first and last words on a page. All the words in between are in ABC order. Decide which words from the box would go on each page. Write the words in ABC order.

effect	countless	figure
commercial	develop	creating

1. camel/cup

_____

_____

_____

2. day/forget

_____

_____

_____

Classifying

Each column groups words about computer artists. Write each word from the box in the group where it belongs.

commercial	images	develop
arrange	figures	

1. What Artists Do

_____

_____

2. What Artists Can Make

_____

_____

Vocabulary in Context

Name _____ Date _____

Word Associations

Write the answer to each question. Use the words from the box.

arrange	commercial	countless	creating
effect	images	motion	television

1. Which word goes with *school pictures?* _____

2. Which word goes with *TV?* _____

3. Which word goes with *cause?* _____

4. Which word goes with *advertisement?* _____

5. Which word goes with *dance?* _____

6. Which word goes with *amount of sand on a beach?*

_____

7. Which word goes with *flowers in a vase?* _____

8. Which word goes with *painting* or *baking?* _____

Unit 7
Vocabulary in Context G3, SV 9780547625768

Vocabulary in Context

Name _____   Date _____

Standardized Test Practice

Read each sentence. Pick the word that best completes the sentence. Circle the letter for the correct word.

TIP

Some tests have letters before the answer choices. Be sure to find the letter of the answer you think is correct and then circle the letter.

1. If you want to get people to buy something, you can write a ____.

   A copy   **C** book

   B model   **D** commercial

2. Numbers and shapes are ____.

   A fingers   **C** places

   B names   **D** figures

3. You can watch movies, sports, and news on a ____.

   A radio   **C** television

   B billboard   **D** protein

4. Today, ____ cartoons is easier than it used to be.

   A counting   **C** crushing

   B causing   **D** creating

5. Computer artists make ____ that move on the screen.

   A partners   **C** images

   B wires   **D** keyboards

6. Before computers, cartoon artists had to draw ____ pictures by hand.

   A ancient   **C** few

   B countless   **D** tiny

7. When something moves, it is in ____.

   A motor   **C** motion

   B television   **D** bound

8. If you work out an idea in detail, you ____ it.

   A develop   **C** expect

   B leave   **D** deliver

Name _____   Date _____

Related Words

There are many words that have to do with movies. Look at each
category and write the words from the box that best fit each group.
Then add your own word to each group.

actors	cartoons	photographers
comedies	animated films	directors

1. Workers

_____

_____

_____

2. Kinds of Motion Pictures

_____

_____

_____

Now try these.

lights	theater	on television
film	cinema	camera

3. Places to See Movies

_____

_____

_____

4. Movie Equipment

_____

_____

_____

Vocabulary in Context G3, SV 9780547625768

Word Skills

Compare and Contrast

Look at each item. Then put a check in the box of each category that fits the item.

	watched	heard	watched at a cinema	watched at home	characters can only be heard
1. motion picture					
2. television show					
3. radio show					

Read and answer each question. Use complete sentences.

4. What are some differences between a motion picture and a radio show?

_____

_____

_____

5. How are television shows and motion pictures alike?

_____

_____

Word Skills

Synonyms

Write each word from the box next to its synonym. Then write an example for each pair of synonyms. The first one is done for you.

| tune | motion picture | gem | theater | performer | cartoon |

	Synonym	Example
1. movie	*motion picture*	*Toy Story*
2. animated film		
3. cinema		
4. actor		
5. song		
6. jewel		

| stream | town | car | creature | sea | street |

7. automobile		
8. road		
9. river		
10. ocean		
11. city		
12. animal		

Word Skills

Name _____ Date _____

Writing

Many commercials are cartoons. What kind of cartoon commercial would you create to get people to go to your favorite restaurant or buy your favorite snack food?

Write a paragraph describing the cartoon commercial. Use some vocabulary words from this unit in your writing.

_____

_____

_____

_____

_____

_____

_____

_____

_____

_____

Writing

Unit 7
Vocabulary in Context G3, SV 9780547625768

Lights, Camera, Action!

Read the passage. Think about the meanings of the boldfaced words. Then go back to the passage. Underline the words or sentences that give you a clue to the meaning of each boldfaced word.

About 12,000 years ago, dogs were wild animals. Then people began to **tame** them. Dogs wanted the food people cooked on their fires. At first, the animals used great **caution**. They were afraid of humans.

As time passed, dogs **gradually** learned to trust people. People then taught dogs to help them. The dogs learned to herd sheep. People also found that they liked to have dogs around for company. Dogs became **companions** to people. Today, some people train dogs for **protection** against anyone who might try to hurt them. **Trainers** teach some dogs to guide people who cannot see. Dogs are even trained to be actors.

Becoming a good dog actor is not easy. A good dog actor must be **intelligent**. It must be smart enough to learn about 90 spoken **commands** and hand signals. You might wonder how a dog is trained to do **dangerous** things such as rescue someone from a burning building. Trainers use praise, and they repeat the commands over and over. Good dog actors catch on quickly and **respond** eagerly.

One dog trainer thinks that some dog actors really do act. Bob Weatherwax has trained many of the dogs that have played Lassie. He says that a good dog actor doesn't just follow commands. It matches the mood of the human actors. The next time you see a dog on the screen, see if you agree. Is it a dog or a real actor at work?

Vocabulary in Context G3, SV 9780547625768

Context Clues

Meanings for the vocabulary words are given below. Go back to the passage and read each sentence that has a vocabulary word. If you still cannot tell the meaning, look for clues in the sentences that come before and after the one with the vocabulary word. Write each word from the box in front of its meaning.

tame	companions	commands	caution	gradually
trainers	intelligent	respond	protection	dangerous

1. _____: to act in answer to

2. _____: people who teach animals

3. _____: great care; interest in safety

4. _____: something that keeps a person from harm

5. _____: happening slowly and steadily

6. _____: not safe

7. _____: those who go along and keep others company

8. _____: to make a wild animal gentle and teach it to obey

9. _____: orders or signals

10. _____: smart

Cloze Paragraph

Use the words in the box to complete the paragraph. Reread the paragraph to be sure it makes sense.

commands	respond	tame
trainers	companions	gradually

Last year we bought two dogs. We did not have to

(1) _____ the dogs, but we had to teach them to trust and

obey us. Like all good (2) _____, we gave them a lot

of praise. At first, the dogs didn't (3) _____ to our

directions very well. We didn't give up, though. As the weeks passed,

they (4) _____ learned more and more. Now they follow

our (5) _____ every time! They have turned out to be

wonderful (6) _____ and friends.

Antonyms

Remember that antonyms are words that have opposite meanings. Match the words in the box with the antonyms listed below. Write each word on the line.

caution	gradually	protection	dangerous	intelligent

1. safe _____

2. stupid _____

3. carelessness _____

4. rapidly _____

5. harm _____

Vocabulary in Context G3, SV 9780547625768

Vocabulary in Context

Word Groups

Read each group of words. Think about how they are alike. Write the word from the box that best completes each word group.

protection	respond	companions	intelligent	gradually

1. slowly, bit by bit, _____

2. friends, pals, _____

3. clever, bright, _____

4. guarding, care, _____

5. answer, reply, _____

Writing Sentences

Use each vocabulary word in the box to write a sentence of your own.

tame	caution	trainers	dangerous	commands

1. _____

2. _____

3. _____

4. _____

5. _____

Word Map

Words can be put on a word map to show what they have in common. Use the vocabulary words in the box to complete the word map about a dog. Add at least one other word that you know to each group.

companions intelligent	commands respond	trainers protection

What Dogs Can Be

_____

_____

What Dogs Can Give

_____

_____

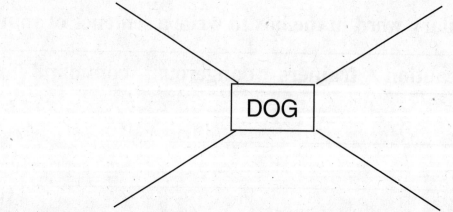

DOG

Who Works with Dogs

_____

_____

What Dogs Can Do or Obey

_____

_____

Standardized Test Practice

Circle the letter for the word or words that have the same or almost the same meaning as the boldfaced word.

TIP

Think about the meaning of the **boldfaced** word before you choose an answer. Don't be fooled by a word that looks like the boldfaced word.

Vocabulary in Context

1. **tame** dogs

   A wash   C make gentle

   B throw   D make wild

2. dog **trainers**

   A teachers   C hunters

   B pictures   D actors

3. learn **gradually**

   A never   C rapidly

   B slowly   D easily

4. **dangerous** work

   A not hard   C not safe

   B safe   D interesting

5. **intelligent** people

   A strong   C stupid

   B smart   D important

6. trainer's **commands**

   A tricks   C orders

   B praise   D songs

7. **respond** eagerly

   A lose   C repair

   B answer   D rescue

8. **companions** to people

   A gifts   C times

   B enemies   D friends

9. for **protection**

   A luck   C trust

   B safety   D presents

10. use **caution**

    A courage   C care

    B energy   D talent

83

Using Context

Read each sentence, paying attention to the underlined word. Then complete the statements about the underlined word.

1. Susan's <u>canine</u> animal barks and wags its tail.

   Canine refers to a _____.

2. John's <u>feline</u> meows when it is hungry.

   A feline is a _____.

3. The <u>porcine</u> animal oinks and eats a lot.

   Porcine refers to a _____.

4. The <u>bovine</u> moos and produces milk.

   A bovine is a _____.

5. The <u>equine</u> animal has a brown mane and a flowing tail.

   Equine refers to a _____

Use each letter of the word to write a word that describes that kind of animal. The word can describe the way the animal looks, acts, or sounds. One example for each animal is done for you.

F furry

E _____

L _____

I _____

N _____

E _____

C _____

A _____

N _____

I _____

N _____

E energetic

Word Skills

Related Words

Many groups of animals have "family names." Dogs are part of the canine family. Cats, including pets and wild cats, are felines. Cows are bovines. Horses are in the equine family.

Underneath each animal family name, draw a picture of an animal that represents it. Then write each word from the box under the correct family. Finally, add your own example for each animal.

dog	lion	steer	colt	cow	wolf
horse	zebra	cattle	coyote	cat	kitten

1. Canine	2. Feline	3. Bovine	4. Equine

Word Skills

Analogies

An analogy shows how pairs of words go together.

Example:
Hot is to *cold* as *day* is to *night*.
(*Hot* is the opposite of *cold*; *day* is the opposite of *night*.)

1. *Porcine* is to *pig* as *canine* is to _____.

2. *Bovine* is to *cow* as *equine* is to _____.

3. *Canine* is to *bark* as *feline* is to _____.

4. *Oink* is to *porcine* as *neigh* is to _____.

5. *Wolf* is to *canine* as *tiger* is to _____.

Now try these.

6. *Calf* is to *cow* as *kitten* is to _____.

7. *Corn* is to *pig* as *hay* is to _____.

8. *Paws* are to *canines* as _____ are to *equines*.

9. *Fur* is to *animals* as _____ are to *birds*.

10. *Snouts* are to *pigs* as _____ are to *people*.

Name _____   Date _____

Writing

Think about what it would be like to be a dog trainer. What kinds of dogs would you like to work with? What would you want to train dogs to do? Write several sentences that tell what you think. Use some vocabulary words from this unit in your writing.

_____

_____

_____

_____

_____

_____

_____

_____

Writing

Vocabulary in Context G3, SV 9780547625768

There Is Music in the Air

Read the passage. Think about the meanings of the boldfaced words. Then go back to the passage. Underline the words or sentences that give you a clue to the meaning of each boldfaced word.

What is music? Music is sound. Sound is made when a material moves back and forth rapidly. Carefully stretch a rubber band between two rulers. Ask someone to snap one side of it. This will **cause** the rubber band to move quickly. It will make a sound.

A guitar is an **instrument** that makes music. If you stretch a guitar string and pluck it, the string will move rapidly and make a soft sound. If you attach the string to a guitar, you'll get a lot more **volume**. Why is the sound louder now? You are moving the string, the wood of the guitar, and the air inside it. If you stretch the string to **tighten** it, you will get a higher sound, like "ping." This is called high **pitch**. If you loosen the string, the pitch will sound lower, like "pong."

A drum is another **musical** instrument. Its sound is made by tapping on a stretched piece of plastic or hide. Some drums are **struck** with sticks. Others are played by pressing foot **pedals**. Drums are the instruments that help keep the **beat**. The beat is the "ONE two, ONE two" part of the music that makes you want to tap your feet.

Music can **communicate** many messages. A fast beat might make you feel happy. A low pitch might make you feel sad. Whatever instrument is used, music has something to say.

Vocabulary in Context G3, SV 9780547625768

Context Clues

Meanings for the vocabulary words are given below. Go back to the passage and read each sentence that has a vocabulary word. If you still cannot tell the meaning, look for clues in the sentences that come before and after the one with the vocabulary word. Write each word from the box in front of its meaning.

cause	volume	tighten	pitch	pedals
instrument	musical	struck	beat	communicate

1. _____ : having to do with music

2. _____ : to receive and send messages

3. _____ : a reason something happens

4. _____ : bars pressed down by the foot

5. _____ : something used to make music

6. _____ : how high or low a sound is

7. _____ : to make tight

8. _____ : how loud a sound is

9. _____ : the part of music you tap your feet to

10. _____ : hit

Name _____ Date _____

Word Sense

Read each phrase. Check the glossary to see if the words make sense together. If they do, write <u>yes</u> on the line. If they do not, write a new word that does make sense with the underlined word.

1. *communicate* jelly _____

2. *musical* stairs _____

3. *tighten* strings _____

4. peanut *pedals* _____

5. *struck* hard _____

6. *cause* time _____

Music Words

The words in the box all have to do with music. Write each word beside its meaning.

volume   beat   pitch   instrument

1. the pattern of loud and soft sounds in music _____

2. the amount of sound _____

3. a tool for making music _____

4. lowness or highness of sound _____

Cloze Paragraph

Use the words in the box to complete the paragraph. Reread the paragraph to be sure it makes sense.

pitch	musical	instrument
beat	tighten	pedals

A tambourine is my favorite (1)_____. It has no strings

to (2) _____. It has no (3) _____ to place

my feet on. I do not worry that the (4) _____ is too high

or too low. I just use my hand to tap the (5) _____ of any

song I hear. Someday I will play one in a (6) _____ show.

Word Associations

Read each question. Answer each question with a word from the box.

cause	communicate	struck	volume	pedals

1. Which word goes with *feet*? _____

2. Which word goes with *telling*? _____

3. Which word goes with *what happened*? _____

4. Which word goes with *hands*? _____

5. Which word goes with *turn it up*? _____

Name _____ Date _____

Word Map

Words can be put on a word map to show what they have in common. Write each word from the box in the group where it belongs to tell about musical instruments.

| pedals | volume | musical | tighten |
| pitch | struck | communicate | |

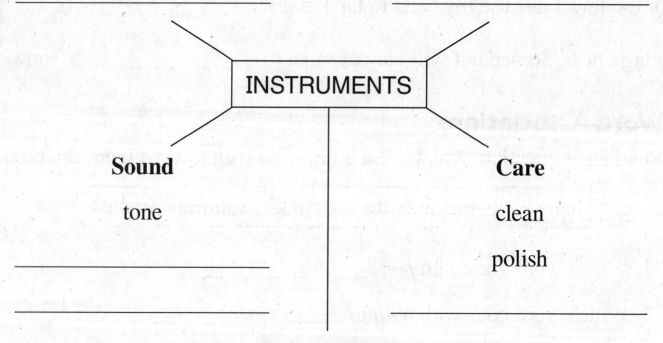

Some Parts

keys

strings

_____

How Played

plucked

used bow

_____

INSTRUMENTS

Sound

tone

_____

_____

Care

clean

polish

_____

Reason Played

own pleasure

_____ ideas

_____ entertainment

Standardized Test Practice

Read each sentence. Pick the word that best completes the sentence. Circle the letter for that word.

Vocabulary in Context

TIP

Before you choose an answer, try reading the sentence with each answer choice. This will help you choose the answer that makes sense.

1. To ____ with her, you will have to write a letter.

   A sad   **C** communicate

   B crying   **D** baker

2. My legs are long enough to reach the ____.

   A going   **C** loud

   B pedals   **D** them

3. He ____ the nail with the hammer.

   A struck   **C** tightened

   B likely   **D** jump

4. The heavy rain will ____ a flood.

   A holds   **C** cause

   B angry   **D** lesson

5. Please ____ your laces before the race starts.

   A beats   **C** tighten

   B struck   **D** faked

6. The high ____ of the flute sounds clear.

   A pedals   **C** lots

   B pitch   **D** shelf

7. The ____ was so low I could not hear it.

   A their   **C** volume

   B lovely   **D** sailing

8. We marched to a steady ____.

   A seated   **C** causes

   B beat   **D** watered

9. Our band will play at the ____ show.

   A musical   **C** silent

   B tree   **D** laughing

10. The drummer was glad to find her lost ____.

    A placed   **C** instrument

    B danced   **D** volume

Related Words

Read each list of words. Think of how they are related. Circle the letter next to the correct topic. Then add a word of your own to each group of words.

1. flute, clarinet, oboe, _____

    A percussion instruments   **C** tools

    B colors   **D** woodwinds

2. fork, spoon, spatula, _____

    A music   **C** utensils

    B foods   **D** songs

3. drum, cymbal, tambourine, _____

    A percussion instruments   **C** woodwinds

    B string instruments   **D** horns

4. hammer, wrench, chisel, _____

    A shapes   **C** percussion instruments

    B workers   **D** devices

5. drummer, pianist, violinist _____

    A woodwinds   **C** musicians

    B percussion instruments   **D** horns

Name _____ Date _____

Onomatopoeia

Onomatopoeia words are words that imitate sounds.

Example: *clank, buzz*

Read each question and illustrate your answer.

1. What kind of percussion instrument might make sounds like *boom* and *wham*?

2. In what kind of weather do you hear sounds like *crackle* and *crash*?

3. What kind of animal makes sounds like *chirp, tweet,* and *twitter*?

Pretend you are at a music concert. Make a list of all the sounds you hear.

_____

_____

_____

Word Skills

Unit 9

Vocabulary in Context G3, SV 9780547625768

Synonyms

Read each sentence. Find a word in the box that is a synonym for the underlined word or words in the sentence. Write the word on the line. The first one is done for you.

| famous | instrument | hear | concert | drums | flute |

1. I love to <u>listen to</u> piano music. _____*hear*_____

2. What kind of <u>tool</u> do you play? _____

3. Rosa plays a <u>woodwind</u>. _____

4. Carlos prefers to play <u>percussion instruments</u>. _____

5. Do you know any <u>well-known</u> musicians? _____

6. I enjoyed attending the <u>performance</u>. _____

Now try these.

| glad | practices | left | bother | tools | utensils |

7. It's not polite to <u>disturb</u> people while they are listening to music.

_____

8. James put <u>forks and spoons</u> on the table. _____

9. Ella used the <u>devices</u> to fix her car. _____

10. We <u>departed</u> when the concert was over. _____

11. She was <u>pleased</u> when she got her new horn. _____

12. The musician <u>rehearses</u> every day. _____

Vocabulary in Context G3, SV 9780547625768

Word Skills

Writing

People play many kinds of instruments to make many kinds of music. Orchestras play many kinds of music. What kind of music do you like to hear most of all? Is it soft and peaceful? Is it loud with lots of drums? Do you enjoy country music the most?

Write a paragraph about your favorite kind of music. Tell why you like it best. If you have two favorite kinds of music, tell about both of them. Use some vocabulary words from this unit in your writing.

_____

_____

_____

_____

_____

_____

_____

_____

Writing

Special Times for Music

**Read the passage. Think about the meanings of the boldfaced words.
Then go back to the passage. Underline the words or sentences that
give you a clue to the meaning of each boldfaced word.**

A feast or party is always a time to **celebrate** with music, song, and
dance. At a Native American **festival** you would hear drums, flutes,
and rattles. You would also see dances and hear **chants**, the singing of
words over and over in a certain pattern.

A Native American **ceremony** also includes music, song, and
dance. This special event may be serious, but that doesn't mean that a
ceremony is quiet.

Long ago, Native Americans began using music, song, and dance
to tell about their daily lives and beliefs. Each **tribe**, or group, held
services and festivals to help it at important times. There were songs
and dances to help sick people get well. There were songs and dances
of **death** when a person died. There were special dances for hunters
to help them catch food, like the Buffalo Dance. Farming tribes held
planting services and **harvest** festivals
when the crops were picked. In
between, they might do rain and sun
dances to help the crops grow.

In many tribes the **elders** taught the
younger people these songs and dances.
Grandparents taught their children's
children. These grandchildren became
teachers, too. In this way, Native
Americans kept the ways of the
ancestors alive.

Name _____ Date _____

Context Clues

Meanings for the vocabulary words are given below. Go back to the passage and read each sentence that has a vocabulary word. If you still cannot tell the meaning, look for clues in the sentences that come before and after the one with the vocabulary word. Write each word from the box in front of its meaning.

chants	festival	tribe	ancestors	elders
celebrate	death	grandparents	ceremony	harvest

1. _____ : a feast; a big party

2. _____ : a serious, special event

3. _____ : songs with words repeated in almost the same tone of voice

4. _____ : when crops are gathered

5. _____ : to honor something with special activities

6. _____ : older people

7. _____ : group of people living together

8. _____ : end of life

9. _____ : family members who lived long ago

10. _____ : the parents of parents

Word Groups

Read each group of words. Think about how they are alike. Write the word from the box that best completes each word group.

> festival   celebrate   grandparent   death

1. mother, father, aunt, _____

2. party, fair, feast, _____

3. perform, enjoy, honor, _____

4. end, stop, finish, _____

Glossary Skills

Read each question. For a "yes" answer, write the word <u>yes</u> on the line. For a "no" answer, write a sentence that gives the correct meaning of the underlined word. Use the Glossary if you need help.

1. Is an <u>ancestor</u> someone who has not been born?

_____

2. Is a <u>harvest</u> the time when crops are picked?

_____

3. Are <u>chants</u> things you can touch with your hands?

_____

4. Is a <u>tribe</u> made up of people who know each other?

_____

Vocabulary in Context

Root Words

The root of the word **celebrate** comes from the Latin *celebratus*, which means "festive and honor." The suffix *-ion* means "act of." That makes a **celebration** the act of celebrating or doing something special for an event.

Build words by adding endings to these root words. Use each word in a sentence of your own.

1. celebrate + *-ing* = _____

_____

2. festive + *-al* = _____

_____

3. ancestor + *-s* = _____

_____

4. grandparent + *-s* = _____

_____

Idea Completion

Complete the following sentences. Use the word in parentheses in your sentence.

1. I heard _____. (chants)

2. We attended _____. (ceremony)

3. The farmer _____. (harvest)

4. A festival _____. (tribe)

5. The end _____. (death)

6. The members _____. (tribe)

Vocabulary in Context

Hidden Message Puzzle

Write a word from the box next to each clue. To find the message, copy the numbered letters in the matching numbered boxes at the bottom of the page. Then you will know other special times for music.

Vocabulary in Context

celebrate	death	elders	festival
ceremony	tribe	chant	

1. kind of song □ □ □ □ □
                        6

2. opposite of birth □ □ □ □ □
                             1

3. feast □ □ □ □ □ □ □ □
              8

4. older people □ □ □ □ □ □
                       5

5. special event □ □ □ □ □ □ □ □
                              2   7

6. a group of people who live together □ □ □ □ □
                                              4

7. to honor □ □ □ □ □ □ □ □ □
                 3

ANSWER: □ □ □ □ □ □ □ □
             1 2 3 4 5 6 7 8

102

Standardized Test Practice

Read the phrase. Look for the word or words that have the same or almost the same meaning as the boldfaced word. Circle the letter for the correct word.

TIP

Always read all the answer choices. Many choices may make sense. Only one answer choice has the same or almost the same meaning as the boldfaced word.

1. loud **chants**

   A sports   C songs

   B events   D charts

2. good **harvest**

   A hair   C crops picked

   B machines   D seeds planted

3. happy **festival**

   A party   C tent

   B studio   D farm

4. let us **celebrate**

   A study   C sleep

   B honor   D announce

5. ancient **ancestors**

   A dreams   C feasts

   B farm   D family
     helpers   members

6. his **grandparents**

   A pals   C teachers

   B actors'   D parents'
     friends   parents

7. group's **elders**

   A children   C older people

   B classmates   D pets

8. person's **death**

   A end   C birth

   B place   D home

9. wedding **ceremony**

   A story   C serious event

   B painting   D puppets

10. Native American **tribe**

    A pride   C language

    B group   D nest

Synonyms

Look in the box for pairs of words that are synonyms. Write a pair of synonyms on each line. The first one is done for you.

beliefs	special	pasture	jump	routines	habits
traditions	ideas	services	unusual	leap	meadow

1. _routines/habits_

2. _____

3. _____

4. _____

5. _____

6. _____

Now try these.

nervous	sparkle	practices	twinkle	trade	plain
assist	habits	ordinary	worried	exchange	help

7. _____

8. _____

9. _____

10. _____

11. _____

12. _____

Word Skills

Using Context

Read each sentence. Then write a definition for the underlined word.

1. One of my <u>habits</u> is to have a good breakfast every morning.

_____

_____

2. Blowing out candles on birthday cakes is a common <u>practice</u>.

_____

_____

3. One of Darnell's <u>beliefs</u> is that it's good to be kind to others.

_____

_____

4. People get married at wedding <u>services</u>.

_____

_____

5. Playing games on Friday night is a <u>tradition</u> in Leshia's family.

_____

_____

Answer the question.

6. What is a tradition you would like to start in your family?

_____

Word Skills

Name _____ Date _____

Word Origins

Tradition comes from a Latin word that means "handing over."
Families "hand over" their traditions to their children.

**Look at the word web below. Fill in as many examples as you can
for each kind of tradition. You could list your family's traditions or
ones you have heard about, read about, or seen on television.**

Places That People Go Every Year
Example: zoo

_____

_____

Holidays That People Celebrate
Example: Kwanzaa

_____

_____

Games That People
Play
Example: dreidel

_____

_____

Traditions

Services That People
Attend
Example: graduations

_____

_____

Food That People Eat at Special Times
Example: cake on birthdays

_____

_____

Writing

You have just learned some ways that Native Americans celebrate. Think about some events that you and your family celebrate.

Write a letter to a friend about something that you celebrate. You may want to invite your friend to join the celebration. Be sure you describe why and how you celebrate. Use some vocabulary words from this unit in your writing.

_____
(Date)

Dear _____,

_____

_____

_____

_____

_____

_____

_____

Sincerely,

_____

      Vocabulary in Context G3, SV 9780547625768

Writing

Glossary

A

ability   *noun*   the power to do something; skill (page 18)

actor   *noun*   someone who performs on stage, in movies, on TV, or on radio (page 74)

adventures   *noun*   exciting or unusual experiences (page 18)

ancestors   *noun*   earlier members of one's family, such as a great-grandfather (page 98)

ancient   *adjective*   very old (page 28)

animated films

   noun   motion pictures made up of a series of drawings with moving figures (page 74)

arrange   *verb*   to put something in a certain position or order (page 68)

athlete   *noun*   person trained in a sport or other activity that takes strength and skill (page 48)

athletic   *adjective*   of, for, or having to do with sports and games (page 64)

audience   *noun*   the group of people who come to a place to see something (page 28)

B

balancing   *adjective*   keeping one's body in a steady position, usually one that is hard to hold (page 48)

beat   *noun*   the pattern of loud and soft sounds in music (page 88)

beginnings   *noun*   time when something began (page 18)

beliefs   *noun*   things in which one has faith or confidence (page 104)

biology	*noun*	the science of life and of the ways in which living things grow, develop, and reproduce (page 44)
bovine	*noun*	a cow, ox, or other related animal (page 84)

C

campfire	*noun*	a fire used at a camp for cooking and warmth (page 18)
canine	*adjective*	belonging to a group of animals that includes dogs, foxes, and wolves (page 84)
career	*noun*	the way a person makes a living; a person's lifework (page 58)
carpenter	*noun*	a person who makes or repairs things, often using wood (page 34)
cartoons	*noun*	motion pictures made by photographing a series of slightly different drawings so that the made-up characters seem to move (pages 58, 74)
cause	*verb*	to make something happen (page 88)
caution	*noun*	great care (page 78)
celebrate	*verb*	to do something special for a certain day or event (page 98)
ceremony	*noun*	a set of acts that are done for special events, such as a wedding or birth (page 98)
challenge	*noun*	something that is hard to do (page 48)
chants	*noun*	short, simple songs sung over and over again (page 98)
characters	*noun*	people or animals in a book, play, or movie (page 58)
cinema	*noun*	a motion picture theater (page 74)

Vocabulary in Context G3, SV 9780547625768

climate	*noun*	the kind of weather a place has (page 8)
comedies	*noun*	amusing plays or shows having a happy ending (page 74)
comic	*adjective*	funny (page 28)
commands	*noun*	orders to do something (page 78)
commercial	*noun*	a message that tries to get people to buy something; an ad (page 68)
communicate	*verb*	to send and receive messages (page 88)
companions	*noun*	friends; those who keep another company (page 78)
compare	*verb*	to find out how two things are the same (page 38)
condition	*noun*	a person's health and strength (page 48)
confidence	*noun*	strong trust (page 48)
costume	*noun*	special clothing worn to look like someone or something else (page 28)
countless	*adjectives*	too many to count (page 68)
creating	*verb*	making (page 68)

D

dangerous	*adjective*	not safe (page 78)
death	*noun*	the end of life (page 98)
delighted	*adjective*	very pleased (page 58)
develop	*verb*	to work out in detail (page 68)
device	*noun*	an instrument or tool (page 94)
difficult	*adjective*	hard to do (page 48)
dinosaurs	*noun*	a type of animal that lived on Earth millions of years ago (page 8)

Vocabulary in Context G3, SV 9780547625768

directors	*noun*	people who are in charge of an activity, such as a play, a movie, or a show on TV or radio (page 74)
distance	*noun*	the space between two things (page 38)
drawings	*noun*	pictures made with pen, pencil, crayon, or chalk (page 58)

E

ecology	*noun*	the relationship of plants and animals to each other and their surroundings (page 44)
effect	*noun*	something that happens because of something else; result (page 68)
elders	*noun*	older people (page 98)
electrician	*noun*	a person who designs, installs, operates, or repairs electrical equipment or machinery (page 34)
enchanted	*adjective*	charmed; very pleased (page 58)
energy	*noun*	the power to work and act (page 28)
entertain	*verb*	to keep people interested; to amuse (page 28)
entertainment	*noun*	something that pleases or interests people (page 58)
equine	*adjective*	of, related to, or like a horse (page 84)
event	*noun*	a happening; something that takes place (page 28)
exhausting	*adjective*	making one very tired (page 48)
extinct	*adjective*	no longer found on Earth (page 8)

F

fantasy	*noun*	a story about things and people that could not be real (page 24)

feline	*noun*	an animal of the cat family (page 84)
festival	*noun*	a special time for celebrating (page 98)
figure	*noun*	shape (page 68)
film	*noun*	a movie (page 74)
fossils	*noun*	the remains of plants or animals of a past age (page 8)

G

glimmering	*adjective*	shining with a faint, unsteady light (page 54)
glistening	*adjective*	shining or sparkling, as with reflected light (page 54)
graceful	*adjective*	having a beautiful form; pleasing (page 48)
gradually	*adverb*	happening slowly and steadily; bit by bit (page 78)
grandparents		
	noun	grandfather and grandmother (page 98)

H

habits	*noun*	an action done repeatedly (page 104)
harvest	*noun*	the gathering of crops (page 98)
height	*noun*	the distance from top to bottom (page 38)
herpetology	*noun*	the science that studies reptiles and amphibians (page 44)
humor	*noun*	what makes something funny (page 58)

I

images	*noun*	likenesses of people, animals, or things (page 68)
imaginary	*adjective*	existing only in the mind; unreal; made-up (pages 18, 24)
increase	*verb*	to grow in size; add to (page 38)

Vocabulary in Context G3, SV 9780547625768

information	*noun*	facts; things that are known (page 8)
instrument	*noun*	something that is used to make music (pages 88, 94)
intelligent	*adjective*	smart; quick to learn (page 78)
intently	*adverb*	with close attention (page 28)

J

jungle	*noun*	hot, wet land with a thick growth of trees and bushes (page 8)

L

laughter	*noun*	sounds people make when they are happy or amused (page 28)
legal	*adjective*	of or having to do with the law (page 64)
legends	*noun*	made-up stories about the past (page 18)
levels	*noun*	layers (page 38)
lizards	*noun*	animals with short legs, scaly skin, long bodies, and long tails (page 8)

M

machinist	*noun*	a person who is skilled in using machine tools (page 34)
mason	*noun*	a person who is skilled in building with materials such as stone, brick, or concrete (page 34)
medical	*adjective*	of or having to do with medicine (page 64)
meter	*noun*	a measure of length, just over 39 inches (page 38)
moist	*adjective*	a little wet; damp (page 8)
motion	*noun*	movement (page 68)

motion picture

	noun	a series of pictures flashed on a screen in rapid succession, making things in the pictures seem to move (page 74)
movie	*noun*	a motion picture (page 74)
muscles	*noun*	the parts of the body used to move other parts (page 48)
musical	*adjective*	able to make music; having to do with music (page 88)

N

numerous	*adjective*	many; great in number (page 38)

O

orchard	*noun*	a piece of land on which many fruit trees are grown (page 18)

P

pear	*noun*	a sweet, juicy, green or yellowish fruit rounded at one end and smaller toward the stem end (page 26)
pedals	*noun*	parts of a machine that are moved by the foot (page 88)
percussion	*noun*	having a tone produced by striking or hitting, as a drum (page 94)
performer	*noun*	a person who entertains the public (page 48)
photographer		
	noun	someone who takes pictures (page 74)
pitch	*noun*	the lowness or highness of a sound (page 88)
plumber	*noun*	a person whose business is installing or repairing water pipes (page 34)

porcine	*adjective*	of or similar to swine or pigs (page 84)
practices	*noun*	a person's customary or usual actions; habits (page 104)
precaution	*noun*	care taken to avoid possible harm or danger (page 14)
preheat	*verb*	to heat something before it is used (page 14)
prehistoric	*adjective*	of or belonging to the time before written history (page 14)
prejudge	*verb*	to judge beforehand, without proper knowledge (page 14)
prepay	*verb*	to pay or pay for in advance (page 14)
preserved	*verb*	kept safe; kept the same for a long time (page 8)
pretend	*verb*	to make believe (page 24)
professional	*adjective*	getting paid to do something others do for fun; expert (page 28)
protection	*noun*	something that keeps one from danger or harm (page 78)

R

respond	*verb*	to act in answer to something said or done (page 78)

S

scoops	*verb*	hollows out by digging (page 18)
services	*noun*	formal ceremonies (page 104)
shimmering	*adjective*	shining with a faint, unsteady light (page 54)
skull	*noun*	the bones of the head (page 8)
sparkling	*adjective*	lively (page 54)
struck	*verb*	past tense of strike; hit (page 88)

studio	*noun*	a place where movies are made (page 58)
supply	*verb*	to give something needed (page 38)

T

tale	*noun*	a story (pages 18, 24)
talent	*noun*	natural skill in art, sports, or some other area (page 58)
tame	*verb*	to train a wild animal to be gentle and to obey (page 78)
technology	*noun*	the application of science and industrial skills to practical uses (page 44)
television	*noun*	a machine that receives signals and shows pictures with sound (page 68)
theater	*noun*	place where people go to see a movie or a play (page 74)
thick	*adjective*	crowded; set close together (page 38)
thousand	*noun*	ten hundred; 1,000 (page 38)
tighten	*verb*	to make tighter; to stretch (page 88)
traditions	*noun*	customs that are passed on from parents to children (page 104)
trainers	*noun*	people who teach tricks to animals (page 78)
tribe	*noun*	a group of people who live together as a community (page 98)
twinkling	*noun*	sparkling or shining (page 54)

U

utensils	*noun*	tools or pieces of equipment used to do something (page 94)

Vocabulary in Context G3, SV 9780547625768

V

volume   *noun*   the amount of sound (page 88)

W

wilderness   *noun*   a wild place where no people live (page 18)

woodwind   *noun*   any of a group of musical wind instruments, such as a clarinet or a flute (page 94)

Y

yarn   *noun*   a story, usually long and exaggerated, that is made up (page 24)

Vocabulary in Context G3, SV 9780547625768

Answer Key

Page 9
1. dinosaurs
2. information
3. preserved
4. fossils
5. skull
6. lizards
7. moist
8. jungle
9. climate
10. extinct

Page 10
Antonyms
1. preserved
2. moist
3. extinct
4. jungle

Dictionary Skills
1. skull
2. lizards
3. fossils
4. climate
5. dinosaur

Page 11
Word Associations
1. skull
2. jungle
3. climate
4. dinosaurs, lizards
5. moist
6. fossils
7. extinct

Writing Sentences
Answers will vary based on students' personal experiences.

Page 12
1. information
2. climate
3. skull
4. jungle
5. moist
6. preserved
7. extinct
Answer: footprints

Page 13
1. B
2. C
3. A
4. C
5. C
6. B
7. D
8. A

Page 14
2. do too much
3. not told
4. pay before
5. not cut
6. judge before
7. wrap again
8. heat before
9. use too much
10. filled again
11. not washed
12. heat too much

Page 15
Accept reasonable answers. Example answers given.
2. cross out warm; washer
3. cross out *magnet*; imagining
4. cross out *careful*; caution

www.harcourtschoolsupply.com
© HMH Supplemental Publishers Inc. All rights reserved.

118

Answer Key
Vocabulary in Context G3, SV 9780547625768

5. cross out *clear*; cleaner

6. cross out *redo*; overuse

7. cross out *parking*; sparkle

8. cross out *underground*; replay

9. cross out *film*; filling

10. cross out *storage*; history

11. cross out *precut*; tested

12. cross out *pain*; overpay

13. cross out *lead*; unload

14. cross out *heal*; reheat

15. cross out *hunter*; hunger

16. cross out *tassle*; tasted

Page 16

1. before history

2. pay before

3. heated before

4. judge before

5. care taken before

6. do again

7. get ready before

8. filled again

Page 17

Answers will vary based on students' personal experiences.

Page 19
Context Clues

1. campfire

2. tale

3. imaginary, wilderness

4. ability, orchard

5. legends

6. adventures, scoops

7. beginnings

Challenge Yourself

Answers will vary.

Page 20
Questions, Reasons, Examples

1. Both are stories.

2. Possible answer: I'd rather have a special ability so I could fly.

3. You would find trees.

4. Possible answer: I'd cook hot dogs on it.

5. adventures

Writing Sentences

Answers will vary.

Page 21

1. imaginary

2. campfires

3. tale

4. orchard

5. scoops

6. legends

7. adventures

8. wilderness

9. beginnings

10. ability

Page 22
Dictionary Skills

1. ability, adventures, beginnings, campfire

2. orchard, scoops, tale, wilderness

Synonyms

1. legends

2. scoops

3. imaginary

4. ability

Page 23

1. A

2. C

3. A

4. D

5. B

6. B

7. C

8. A

9. D

10. B

Vocabulary in Context G3, SV 9780547625768

Page 24

1.–3. Answers will vary. Accept reasonable answers.

4. Possible answers: kings, queens, princes

5. Accept reasonable answers. Make sure character name fits picture.

Page 25

1. five
2. No. The dictionary says a *yarn* is made up.
3. *Yarn* has two meanings; each one is numbered.
4. Possible answer: My friend likes to pretend she's my sister.
5. imaginary
6. It comes after the other two words in ABC order.

Page 26

1. our
2. hour
3. pear
4. pair
5. stair
6. stare
7. hole
8. whole
9. tail
10. tale

Page 27

Answers will vary based on students' personal experiences.

Page 29

Context Clues

1. entertain
2. ancient
3. energy
4. audience
5. event
6. comic
7. costume
8. professional

9. intently
10. laughter

Challenge Yourself

Answers will vary. Possible answers: Mickey Mouse, Bugs Bunny

Page 30

Understanding Multiple-Meaning Words

1. b
2. a
3. a
4. b

Cloze Paragraph

1. event
2. costume
3. entertain
4. audience
5. laughter

Page 31

Answers will vary. Possible answers:

1. when acting in a play
2. when a movie is funny
3. in a funny movie
4. eruption of Mount Vesuvius
5. when they won't sit still in their seats
6. worked on these vocabulary exercises

Page 32

Across

1. professional
4. energy
5. ancient
7. intently
9. entertain

Down

2. event
3. laughter
5. audience
6. costume
8. comic

Vocabulary in Context G3, SV 9780547625768

Page 33

1. D
2. B
3. B
4. A
5. C
6. C
7. B
8. D

Page 34

2. D, tools
3. B, building materials
4. C, fruits
5. D, playground equipment
6. A, breakfast foods
7. C, people who fix things
8. B, things to drink
9. D, things you write with
10. C, coins

Page 35

1. wood
2. flowers
3. trees
4. pipes
5. watch
6. machines
7. short
8. wear
9. sour

Page 36

Answers will vary. Possible answers:

1. that a carpenter works with wood instead of stone
2. they are both building materials
3. that a plumber fixes water pipes instead of electrical equipment
4. they both describe something old
5. they are both eating utensils
6. that a cabin is smaller and more roughly built than a mansion
7. they are both musical instruments
8. that it is smaller and has fresh water instead of salt water
9. that a quarter is worth more than a dime

Page 37

Answers will vary based on students' personal experiences.

Page 39
Context Clues

1. numerous
2. height
3. increase
4. meter
5. thousand
6. supply
7. distance
8. compare
9. thick
10. levels

Challenge Yourself

Answers will vary. Possible answers:

1. my height, my classroom
2. ages, height

Page 40
Synonyms

1. increases
2. numerous
3. supply
4. levels

Writing Sentences

Answers will vary.

Page 41

1. meter
2. compare
3. numerous
4. supply
5. thousand

Answer Key
Vocabulary in Context G3, SV 9780547625768

6. increase

7. distance

8. thick

9. height

10. levels

Answer: many snakes

Page 42

Answers will vary. Possible answers:

levels: heights, sizes, stages, measures

distance: far, near, apart, travel

numerous: many, lots, numbers, thick

Page 43

1. A

2. C

3. A

4. D

5. C

6. B

7. C

8. B

9. A

10. A

Page 44

Additional words will vary. Accept reasonable answers.

1. herpetology: reptiles, alligators, snakes

2. ecology: environment, habitat, relationships

3. technology: computers, microchips, software

4. biology: trees, flowers, mammals

5. archaeology: culture, ancient cities, ruins

Page 45

1. C

2. two

3. noun

4. ecologist

5. someone who studies how living things relate to their surroundings

6. Possible answer: The forest ecology is protected in this park.

7. Possible answer: The ecologist studied the effects of the forest fire on the forest.

Page 46

1. ecology, the study of the environment

2. biology, the study of living things

3. archaeology, the study of ancient times and cultures

4. herpetology, the study of reptiles

5. chronologist, a person who studies the measurement of time

6. psychologist, a person who studies the mind and the way it works

7. Possible answers: technology, nutritionist, specialist, scientist, geology

Page 47

Answers will vary based on students' personal experiences.

Page 49

1. athlete

2. difficult, balancing

3. condition

4. muscles

5. graceful

6. confidence

7. challenge

8. performer

9. exhausting

Page 50

Synonyms

1. exhausting

2. confidence

3. difficult

4. athlete

Glossary Skills

1. having a beautiful form; pleasing

2. something that is hard to do

3. a person who entertains the public

4. keeping one's body in a steady position, usually one that is hard to hold

5. a person's health and strength

6. the parts of the body used to move other parts

7. strong trust

8. making one very tired

Page 51

What She Is: a <u>performer</u>, an <u>athlete</u>

What She Has: body <u>muscles</u>, <u>confidence</u> in herself

What She Faces: big <u>challenges</u>, <u>exhausting</u> work

What Kind of Tricks She Does: difficult/<u>balancing</u> tricks, <u>balancing/difficult</u> acts

What She Has to Be: very <u>graceful</u>, in good <u>condition</u>

Page 52

Add –ing

1. balancing; Answers will vary.

2. exhausting; Answers will vary.

Questions, Reasons, Examples

Answers will vary based on students' personal experiences.

Page 53

1. C
2. C
3. B
4. A
5. C
6. C
7. B
8. A
9. C
10. D

Page 54

1. sparkling
2. fluffy
3. twinkling

4. enormous
5. glimmering
6. sluggish
7. shimmering
8. glistening
9. fierce
10. delicious

Page 55

1. sparkles; sparkled; sparkling
2. twinkles; twinkled; twinkling
3. glimmers; glimmered; glimmering
4. glistens; glistened; glistening

Page 56

glare: harsh, uncomfortable, bright, fierce, burn

both: shine

shimmer: gentle, soft, twinkling, glistening, sparkling, glimmering

Page 57

Answers will vary based on students' personal experiences.

Page 59

1. career
2. studio
3. drawings
4. delighted
5. entertainment
6. cartoons
7. enchanted
8. characters
9. humor
10. talent

Page 60

Cloze Paragraph

1. talent
2. characters
3. delighted
4. Cartoons
5. studio

6. entertainment

Writing Sentences

Answers will vary.

Page 61
Word Groups

1. career
2. drawings
3. talent
4. delighted

Dictionary Skills

1. career, cartoons, characters
2. enchanted, entertainment, humor

Page 62

What He Created Himself: characters, cartoons, drawings

How He Made People Feel: enchanted, delighted

What Helped Him Succeed: humor, talent

Where He Worked: entertainment, studio

Page 63

1. D
2. A
3. C
4. D
5. C
6. B
7. D
8. A
9. B
10. B

Page 64

Drawings will vary.

Additional words will vary. Accept reasonable responses.

1. coach, trainer, referee, basketball player
2. doctor, nurse, surgeon, paramedic
3. lawyer, paralegal, legal secretary
4. actor, actress, singer, comedian

Page 65

Answers will vary. Accept reasonable responses.

Page 66

1. career
2. car
3. chariots
4. carriage
5. carry
6. career

Sentences will vary. Accept reasonable responses.

Page 67

Answers will vary based on students' personal experiences.

Page 69

1. images
2. develop
3. television
4. motion
5. commercial
6. countless
7. arrange
8. figure
9. creating
10. effect

Page 70
Cloze Paragraph

1. television
2. commercial
3. countless
4. creating

Understanding Multiple-Meaning Words

1. b
2. a

Page 71
Dictionary Skills

1. commercial, countless, creating
2. develop, effect, figure

Vocabulary in Context G3, SV 9780547625768

Classifying

1. develop, arrange
2. commercial, images, figures

Page 72

1. images
2. television
3. effect
4. commercial
5. motion
6. countless
7. arrange
8. creating

Page 73

1. D
2. D
3. C
4. D
5. C
6. B
7. C
8. A

Page 74

Additional words will vary. Accept reasonable answers.

1. actors, directors, photographers
2. comedies, animated films, cartoons
3. cinema, theater, on television
4. camera, film, lights

Page 75

1. check watched, heard, watched at a cinema, watched at home
2. check watched, heard, watched at home
3. check heard, characters can only be heard
4. Possible answer: A motion picture has pictures and sound while a radio show only has sound.
5. Possible answer: Both television shows and motion pictures have stories, pictures, and sound.

Page 76

Examples will vary. Accept reasonable answers.

2. cartoon
3. theater
4. performer
5. tune
6. gem
7. car
8. street
9. stream
10. sea
11. town
12. creature

Page 77

Answers will vary based on students' personal experiences.

Page 79

1. respond
2. trainers
3. caution
4. protection
5. gradually
6. dangerous
7. companions
8. tame
9. commands
10. intelligent

Page 80

Cloze Paragraph

1. tame
2. trainers
3. respond
4. gradually
5. commands
6. companions

Antonyms

1. dangerous
2. intelligent

3. caution

4. gradually

5. protection

Page 81
Word Groups

1. gradually

2. companions

3. intelligent

4. protection

5. respond

Writing Sentences
Answers will vary.

Page 82
Additional words will vary. Accept reasonable responses.

What Dogs Can Be: companions, intelligent

What Dogs Can Give: protection

Who Works with Dogs: trainers

What Dogs Can Do or Obey: respond, commands

Page 83
1. C

2. A

3. B

4. C

5. B

6. C

7. B

8. D

9. B

10. C

Page 84
1. dog

2. cat

3. pig

4. cow

5. horse

Describing words will vary. Accept reasonable responses.

Page 85
Drawings will vary.

Examples will vary. Accept reasonable responses.

1. dog, wolf, coyote

2. cat, kitten, lion

3. steer, cow, cattle

4. horse, colt, zebra

Page 86
1. dog

2. horse

3. meow

4. equine

5. feline

6. cat

7. horse

8. hooves

9. feathers

10. noses

Page 87
Answers will vary based on students' personal experiences.

Page 89
1. musical

2. communicate

3. cause

4. pedals

5. instrument

6. pitch

7. tighten

8. volume

9. beat

10. struck

Page 90
Word Sense
New words will vary. Accept reasonable responses. Sample responses given.

1. communicate feelings

2. musical notes

Vocabulary in Context G3, SV 9780547625768

3. yes

4. drum pedals

5. yes

6. cause problems

Music Words

1. beat

2. volume

3. instrument

4. pitch

Page 91
Cloze Paragraph

1. instrument

2. tighten

3. pedals

4. pitch

5. beat

6. musical

Word Associations

1. pedals

2. communicate

3. cause

4. struck

5. volume

Page 92

Some Parts: pedals

How Played: struck

Sound: pitch, volume

Care: tighten

Reason Played: communicate, musical

Page 93

1. C

2. B

3. A

4. C

5. C

6. B

7. C

8. B

9. A

10. C

Page 94

Additional words will vary. Possible answers:

1. D, recorder

2. C, whisk

3. A, xylophone

4. D, screwdriver

5. C, guitarist

Page 95

Illustrations may vary. Accept reasonable answers.

Accept reasonable answers to the list of sounds.

Page 96

2. instrument

3. flute

4. drums

5. famous

6. concert

7. bother

8. utensils

9. tools

10. left

11. glad

12. practices

Page 97

Answers will vary based on students' personal experiences.

Page 99

1. festival

2. ceremony

3. chants

4. harvest

5. celebrate

6. elders

7. tribe

8. death

Vocabulary in Context G3, SV 9780547625768

9. ancestors

10. grandparents

Page 100
Word Groups
1. grandparent
2. festival
3. celebrate
4. death

Glossary Skills
Possible answers:
1. It is a family member who lived long ago.
2. yes
3. They are songs with special patterns.
4. yes

Page 101
Root Words
Sentences will vary but should illustrate an understanding of each word's meaning.
1. celebrating
2. festival
3. ancestors
4. grandparents

Idea Completion
Sentences will vary.

Page 102
1. chant
2. death
3. festival
4. elders
5. ceremony
6. tribe
7. celebrate

Answer to puzzle: holidays

Page 103
1. C
2. C
3. A
4. B

5. D
6. D
7. C
8. A
9. C
10. B

Page 104
2. beliefs/ideas
3. special/unusual
4. services/traditions
5. jump/leap
6. pasture/meadow
7. ordinary/plain
8. worried/nervous
9. twinkle/sparkle
10. practices/habits
11. trade/exchange
12. assist/help

Page 105
Exact wording will vary. Possible answers are given.
1. an action done regularly
2. something that has become an accepted custom by many people
3. something thought to be true
4. formal acts performed in a set manner
5. a custom or set of practices
6. Answers will vary. Accept reasonable answers.

Page 106
Answers will vary. Accept reasonable answers.

Page 107
Answers will vary based on students' personal experiences.